An Inquiry into the Uses of
Instructional Technology

AN INQUIRY INTO
THE USES OF
INSTRUCTIONAL
TECHNOLOGY

James W. Armsey
Norman C. Dahl

A FORD FOUNDATION REPORT

THE FORD FOUNDATION
320 East 43rd Street, New York, N.Y. 10017

Contents

CHAPTER FIVE

The Conditions of Success

Introduction

In the Spring of 1971, the Ford Foundation initiated a study of the current and possible future uses of instructional technology. In the inquiry, James W. Armsey and Norman C. Dahl, two Foundation program advisors, examined the different interpretations of instructional technology, the techniques and devices of instructional technology, some of the major applications in the developed and developing nations, and some of the factors which affect the chances for success.

The Foundation had been active since its beginnings in the early 1950s in domestic support of instructional technology, primarily instructional television, and for more than a decade in attempts to assist efforts in the developing countries to employ technology to help meet quickening demands for expansion of education. The study was commissioned primarily to provide the Foundation itself with guidance for future support of efforts to apply technology to learning, both in the developing countries and in the United States. The report which Messrs. Armsey and Dahl prepared for internal Foundation needs contained considerable information and analysis, which, we believe, would be of interest to a wider audience, and the authors have adapted it for that purpose.

In this study the term instructional technology was defined as the "things of learning," the devices and the materials which are used in the processes of learning and education. Although Messrs. Armsey and Dahl have limited their interpretation of instructional technology to the things of learning, others have both extended and revised it. Some use the term educational technology rather than instructional technology and intend a vastly different meaning. Others employ both terms and distinguish between the two. Frequently the reader or listener will find that he and the writer or speaker envision two tangentially related or completely disparate fields of instructional technology. Because the choice of terms is not merely a point of semantics, chapter one examines some of the representative interpretations and definitions.

In chapter two, several issues which should be of concern to the potential user of instructional technology are discussed. Projects are often inaugurated without any definitive articulation of purpose, without the involvement of the participants, particularly teachers, without careful attention to technological elements of the project, and without a thorough, ordered method of evaluation. The lack of any of these conditions will militate strongly against the success of the project; projects in instructional technology often lack several, and thus the record of their use has not always been outstanding.

In chapter three, the things of learning—the hardware and the software—and their past effectiveness in education are surveyed. The things of learning are being used in both the developed and the developing countries; in chapter four, some of the major applications are reported. Despite the problems that lurk in readiness to beset the unwary user, instructional technology can benefit the students, the teachers, and the educational process. In several projects, the things of learning, including instructional television—the most acclaimed, the most maligned, and the most frequently employed—have been used very successfully. In chapter five, the conditions which appear to increase the likelihood of success are set forth.

The authors brought to their study extensive experience and insight into education and the actual and potential role of technology in education. Mr. Armsey is a veteran observer of and participant in higher education and instructional technology. Before joining the Foundation he was a high-ranking administrator at the Illinois Institute of Technology and at New York University. Among his responsibilities at the Foundation, he was for ten years chief program officer for grants in educational television. Mr. Dahl has extensive experience in education, technology, and international development. Before joining the Foundation he was a professor of mechanical engineering at the Massachusetts Institute of Technology. He has served as a consultant or participant in educational and technological affairs for the U.S. Government, UNESCO, and other agencies. He also has assisted in the development of engineering schools in India, Saudi Arabia, and Afghanistan.

Instructional technology is a moving target, in part because of the changing nature of the technology itself, and in part because of the varying interpretations of its effectiveness and importance. It is a concept that arouses strong emotions among both its advocates and its adversaries. Some theoreticians conceive of instructional technology as supplementary to the teacher; others, anticipating a more active role, see it as a replacement for the traditional teacher. Despite the depth of feeling that it evokes and its increasing prominence, the field is enshrouded in vague definitions, hazy purposes, and murky evaluations.

This is the result of a variety of factors: different interpretations of the field itself; confused and conflicting objectives; too much emphasis on technology for its own sake; too many inflated promises by the "hardware" people; too little attention to the quality of the "software"; overt, covert, and sustained resistance by the teaching establishment; lack of rigor and specificity in research; failure to follow through on demonstrations; and a reluctance to use technology *in place of* rather than as *an additive to* what is already in progress. Such unwillingness simultaneously sustains pockets of sabotage in the existing system and creates cost levels that cannot be sustained.

The purposes are usually multiple. They include: to improve instruction (qualitative); to educate more people (quantitative); to learn about learning (research); to reform the curriculum (substance); to improve the process (method); and to articulate the system (structure). While these are all laudable objectives, when they are intermingled at the beginning they are difficult to separate at the end. The state of the art might be more rapidly advanced if the proponents of research projects, experiments, or demonstrations were required to state clearly and unambiguously their purposes before the project's inception, to adhere to them while the project is underway, and to measure their achievement after the project is completed.

We hope this book will be useful to those seeking to advance the state of the art.

David E. Bell,
Executive Vice President
Vice President/International Division
Harold Howe ii,
Vice President/Division of Education and Research

CHAPTER ONE

Definitions and Terminology

Much of the confusion that surrounds "instructional technology" derives from the ambiguity of its definition. Although in this study instructional technology is defined as the things of learning, other definitions abound. The different terms—educational technology, instructional technology, or the technology of education—are neither synonomous nor analogous; indeed, they reflect different concepts and philosophies. The numerous definitions confuse the reader and the listener and frustrate his ability to understand as well as to evaluate.

Definitions of instructional technology are replete with such amorphous terms as process, system, systematic method, design, evaluation, analysis, mediation, communications, management, utilization, implementation, hardware and software (the "in" terms of technology), and a host of other words that have found acceptance or at least currency in the jargon of the education establishment.

It seems somewhat paradoxical that terms such as instructional or educational technology—which connote scientific precision—should be open to such wide and varied interpretation. In their desire to avoid restricting instructional technology to rigid confines, many of its interpreters employ a broad, sweeping definition. J.R. Gass, director of OECD's Centre for Educational Research and Innovation, defines educational technology as "the organized design and implementation of learning systems taking advantage of but not expecting miracles from modern communications methods, visual aids, classroom organization, and teaching methods."[1] Mr. Gass's views in Paris are reiterated across the channel where Britain's National Council on Educational Technology concluded in a 1971 Working Paper that educational technology "involves the application of systems, techniques, and aids to improve the process of human learning." NCET expanded this description:

It is characterized by four features in particular: the definition of objectives to be achieved by the learner; the application of principles of learning to the analysis and structuring of the subject matter to be learned; the selection and use of the appropriate media for presenting material; and the use of the appropriate methods of assessing student performance to evaluate the effectiveness of courses and materials.[2]

While the generalists espouse the use of the media, they do not see it as the end, but rather as the way to, in Henri Dieuzeide's words, "optimize the learning process." Dieuzeide (Director of UNESCO's Division of Methods, Materials, and Techniques) includes in the realm of educational technology, "all the intellectual and operational efforts made during recent years to regroup arrange, and systematize the application of scientific methods to the organization of new sets of equipment and material. . . ."[3]

These comprehensive definitions, however, cause vague uneasiness among other theoreticians. The search for greater specificity impels some to divide educational technology into several components; others, to distinguish between educational technology and instructional technology; and still others, to remove themselves entirely and consider educational technology an area of curriculum development.

Michael Eraut of the University of Sussex distinguishes four different conceptions of educational technology: the use of machines in education; a technology of instruction; curriculum development; and the management of education.[4] For Robert Silverman there are two kinds of educational technology: relative, which emphasizes procedures and/or devices; and constructive, which deals with analysis of instructional problems and the construction or selection of instruments for evaluation and of techniques or devices to produce the desired outcomes.[5] While Eraut and Silverman distinguish among different kinds of educational technology, a UNESCO report considers the difference between educational and instructional technology to be dependent on size and duration. In this view educational technology refers to projects that are large scale and involve long periods of time while instructional technology refers to shorter term projects that are on a smaller scale. However, the report concludes, "In terms of the process involved, the terms should be considered synonomous."[6] Dragoljub Najman (Director of UNESCO's Division of Educational Studies and Teacher Education) differentiates in terms of function that educational technology and instructional technology have in the classroom: educational technology provides "general support to the teachers"... whereas instructional technology "carries a definite part of the curriculum to the student at regular intervals; it is the use of machines, that is media and services to transfer knowledge."[7]

MacKenzie states that the University of Sussex's Centre for Educational Technology might as well be called the center for curriculum development because, "it is moving away from a fascination with equipment and toward curricular reform, development of learning materials and a concern with technique and process."[8] With Eraut and Jones, he considers that educational technology can be interpreted in two ways: "the use of technology *in* education ..., [which] is concerned with increasing the use of equipment, and as a concept, the technology *of* education, [which is concerned with] improving the effectiveness of learning. . . ."[9]

In the United States, Bright reaffirms this determination not to limit what he terms "educational technology" to hardware. He considers it an instructional theory or approach which may or may not involve hardware.[10]

Yet the National Academy of Engineering's Instructional Technology Committee on Education defines educational technology as the "body of knowledge resulting from the application of the science of teaching and learning to the real world of the classroom, together with the tools and methodologies developed to assist in these applications. . . ." Thus for them, and for others who share their views, the *things* of learning are an essential part of educational technology.

The distinction drawn by the Commission on Instructional Technology represents an attempt to encompass present reality and future promise, to fix upon the concrete without limiting either the scope or reach of instructional technology.

Instructional technology can be defined in two ways. In its more familiar sense it means the media born of the communications revolution which can be used for instructional purposes alongside the teacher, textbook, and blackboard. In general, the Commission's report follows this usage. In order to reflect present day reality, the Commission has had to look at the pieces that make up instructional technology: television, films, overhead projectors, computers and the other items of "hardware" and "software."

... In nearly every case, those media have entered education more in isolation than in combination.

The second and less familiar definition of instructional technology goes beyond any particular medium or device. In this sense, instructional technology is more than the sum of its part. It is a systematic way of designing, carrying out, and evaluating the total process of learning and teaching in terms of specific objectives, based on research in human learning and communication and employing a combination of human and nonhuman resources to bring about more effective instruction. The widespread acceptance and application of this definition belongs to the future.[12]

While the meanings are broad and varied, the practical applications are usually quite narrow. When the terms "educational technology" or "instructional technology" are used—and they are frequently used interchangeably—what is usually meant is television, a talking picture created and delivered electronically by over the air broadcast, telephone lines, microwave, cable or satellite. If the discussion concerns some other kind of method of technology, the writer or speaker usually employs the more precise term.

The Commission's definitions are usually employed in the United States. Abroad, however, in England at the Centre in Sussex and at NCET and in France at OECD's Centre for Educational Research and Innovation, there is a persistent effort to broaden the definition to include everything from planning through post-project evaluation.

Regardless of the interpretations, educational technology or instructional technology is neither an end in itself nor a concept that embraces all of education. Rather, it is a means to accomplish some predetermined, clearly defined, and unambiguously educational objectives.

Notes

1. J. R. Gass, Interview December 9, 1971.
   Educational Technology, The Design and Implementation of Learning Systems, Report based on the results of a workshop organized by CERI in conjunction with the British, Dutch, German and Swedish authorities at Leiden, Netherlands, April 1970, OECD, 1970, p. 7.
2. K. G. Collier, H. P. R. Hodge, T. F., Horton and M. Rathborn, *Colleges of Education Learning Programmes: A Proposal,* Working Paper No. 5, National Council for Educational Technology, 1971, p. 16.
3. Henri Dieuzeide, "Educational Technology: Sophisticated, Adapted and Rational Technology," Series B: Opinions, No. 30, International Commission on the Development of Education, UNESCO, 1971, p. 1.

4. Michael Eraut, "Educational Technology and the Training of Teachers," A final report to the Department of Education and Science from the Centre for Educational Technology, University of Sussex, Brighton, March 1971, p. 5.

5. Robert E. Silverman, "Two Kinds of Technology," *Educational Technology,* January 15, 1968, p. 3.

6. *New Methods and Techniques in Teacher Training,* Final Report of the Meeting of Chief Technical Advisers, National Directors and UNESCO Specialists in Methods and Techniques from UNDP/UNESCO Assisted Teacher-Training Colleges, Paris, December 1969, p. 29.

7. Dragoljub Najman, Interview, December 7, 1971.

8. Norman MacKenzie, Interview, May 24, 1971.

9. Norman MacKenzie, Michael Eraut and Hywel C. Jones, *Teaching and Learning; An Introduction to New Methods and Resources in Higher Education,* UNESCO and the International Association of Universities, Paris, 1970, p. 139.

10. R. Louis Bright, "Educational Technology as an Approach," *Educational Technology,* January 15, 1968, p. 8.

11. "Educational Technology in Higher Education: The Promises and Limitations of ITV and CAI," Instructional Technology Committee of the Commission on Education of the National Academy of Engineering, Washington, D.C., September 1969, p. 1.

12. Commission on Instructional Technology, *To Improve Learning,* A Report to the President and the Congress of the United States, March 1970, Chapter II, p. 19.

CHAPTER TWO

Principal Considerations

Once a working definition has been agreed upon, several factors must be considered. Most important are the purposes for the use of instructional technology. Some of the most disastrous attempts to use the things of learning occur because definite goals are not set forth. Without such direction, a project is doomed to flounder. But no project can fulfill all purposes, despite the pressures applied by various interests. Through a thorough, logical process, the purpose must be chosen, and priorities determined. Once these policy decisions have been made, the techniques and agencies through which the purpose can be achieved become the primary concern. These issues include the selection of the particular instructional technology and its use in the learning environment. The greatest single impediment to the successful implementation of the things of learning appears to be the resistance of classroom teachers. Their support is essential; their reluctance and refusal, disastrous. Other major considerations are the questions of hardware and software, the choice of media, and evaluation of the research.

Purposes and Priorities

As the use of increasingly sophisticated things of learning accelerates, theoreticians and practitioners must consider the purposes to which they will be put. Frequently, the numerous, sometimes contradictory purposes represent a compromise—the efforts of harried, yet determined policymakers to acknowledge and respond to diverse pressures. Major pressures exerted for the use of instructional technology are the impetus for change and the search for both greater educational opportunity and improved education at the same or lower cost per unit.

The purposes ascribed by the educationists to the uses of instructional technology are numerous and, like other concepts, dependent on the motives and aspirations of the planners. The Commission on Instructional Technology summarized the potential benefits (purposes) as follows: to make education more productive and more individual, to give instruction a more scientific base, and to make instruction more powerful, learning more immediate, and access to education more equal.[1]

Hilliard Jason says: "The current major uses of technology can be seen as falling into four categories which derive from the requirements. They are the processes of (1) transmitting information, (2) serving as role models, (3) assisting with the practice of specific skills, and (4) contributing to the provision of feedback."[2]

"The new media appear to bear precisely upon four key objectives," in the view of MacKenzie and his colleagues: "the need to reach more students, to reach them with an improved range of learning materials, to offer greater opportunities for independent study, and to permit at least a limited student response."[3]

Occasionally, a single purpose is paramount; e.g., "a medium for floating information to people who want it,"[4] or "to make up for the great shortage of qualified teachers."[5] More often, there are multiple reasons concerned with quantity, quality, and the system in which teaching and learning occurs. Dieuzeide puts the three this way:[6]

The general tendency is first of all to assign quantitative goals to educational technology: for instance, an existing service is taken over by a technological apparatus ensuring equal quality at lower cost (e.g., setting up language laboratories in training institutions). Still more frequently the aim is to extend educational services to areas previously without them, either at lower costs than those which could be provided by the extension of conventional services (e.g., providing educational services for remote rural areas by a television satellite), or at the same cost as that of conventional ones, but with sufficient savings to justify using the new techniques.

To be sure, qualitative objectives, either manifest or implied, likewise emerge. For instance, the idea may be to introduce new contents into an educational system, modify its basic methods, or raise the individual teacher's qualifications. . . .

In certain cases, educational technology has come to be used as a remedy for inherent deficiencies in the system. . . . In other cases the aim has been to extend the field of action of the traditional system to cover new sectors of the public who could not be reached by existing institutions. . . . Finally, in other instances the aim has been to eliminate the maladjustments between the school and the social environment by trying, through the use of radio and television in particular, to make up for the cultural handicaps of certain categories of pupils.[7]

Intense, conflicting pressures and multiple, sometimes opposing, purposes combine to create a set of circumstances in which instructional technology is often used too quickly, comprehensively, superficially, or inappropriately.

Because it is neither desirable nor possible to do everything at once, the process of decision involves a choice of priorities. Undoubtedly more scrupulous attention to the process in which a program was chosen would decrease costly and disappointing experience with the things of learning.

The term "process" is used in several contexts. At one end of the spectrum is the process of systems analysis, which raises three main questions about an organization's activities: (1) What are the objectives to be reached? (2) How can the objectives be reached most effectively? (3) How do we know when the objectives have been reached?[8]

Engler says that "Learning Systems," "Educational Technology," and "Instructional Systems" can all be defined in three ways: as hardware, as multi-media, and as process. Of the last, he says: "This conception of learning systems usually includes procedures which require highly specific instructional objectives, the selection of instructional strategies based on some kind of task analysis, and empirical development."[9]

Locke criticizes the "cart before the horse approach" and contends that ". . . instead of concentrating so single-mindedly on *products* for sale to schools, we should concern ourselves with the *processes* by which skills and knowledge are acquired."[10]

If the term "process" is applied specifically to the electronic things of learning, Blakely's statement is elucidating: "The organized management of the electronic communications process," he says, "has been described as involving several interrelating steps— (1) formulation of objectives; (2) the designing of programs; (3) the production; (4) the transmission/distribution; (5) reception/playback; and (6) evaluation of results.[11]

Christiansen urges ten specific steps in determining the use of instructional technology:

> . . . identify educational needs
> . . . identify potential users
> . . . solicit the support of potential using agencies and consult responsible representatives of these agencies
> . . . assess what's already available to potential users
> . . . bring together "content" people
> . . . develop new materials
> . . . field-test and revise the materials
> . . . distribute the materials
> . . . evaluate their use
> . . . update and reissue the materials.[12]

"Educational materials, the products of technology, cannot be exported intact to less developed countries," he warns. "Only the process by which materials are created may be exported by the developed countries."

As the effect of teacher resistance illustrates, Oettinger is correct when he urges attention in the process to ascertaining who wants to do it and, equally critical, who does *not* want to do it.[13]

If the objective is to sell instructional technology, *per se,* it is a job for advertising and public relations techniques. If the objective is educational, the specifics must be stated first. When they are, maybe instructional technology is unwarranted. If it is warranted, objectives must be related to present practice, future intention, available resources, and points of support and opposition.

Priorities can be determined only through this diagnostic process. Establishment of priorities requires consideration of the availability of resources, the political, social, and educational situations in the society, any previously established priorities, and the mix of forces for and against the proposed line of action.

Teacher Resistance

According to the literature of instructional technology and the experience of both the users and producers of the things of learning, teachers in the classroom tend to resists technology, especially and primarily television, for several reasons: (1) most important, the basic conservatism of the education establishment; (2) fear of the effects of instructional technology on their role and responsibilities;

(3) the ineptitude and sensitivity of the hardware people; and (4) the minimal or non-existent involvement of teachers at every stage of the process.

In discussing the conservatism of the education establishment, Beeby identified five conditions which inhibit teacher acceptance of innovation: ambiguity of the goals of education, making teachers hesitant to experiment; misunderstanding or misinterpretation of new reforms; identification with the traditional system; isolation from other teachers; and a wide range in teacher effectiveness and adaptability.[14]

A second major reason for teacher resistance lies in their apprehension engendered by the things of learning. Teachers are hesitant to acquire new responsibility which they may not be professionally equipped to handle;[15] they fear that technology may be teacher replacers instead of "teacher extenders."[16] They worry they may lose what they regard as "the essence of professional being."[17] The teacher fears competition from an inhuman, unbeatable adversary.[18] With instructional technology, they envision[19] invasion of their authority in the classroom, and the concomitant loss of autonomy and professional privacy, separation from the student;[20] and, subsequently, downgraded position, loss of recognition and prestige, and reduced rewards.

Psychologically and materially, teachers want from life and work much the same as everyone else. They see their traditional pattern of work threatened and their future made uncertain by the introduction of instructional technology.

Teachers know or sense that the teaching role will be changed by technology. "They are more and more required to become diagnosticians, program developers, and managers of instructional activities."[21] But it does not necessarily follow that as the teacher is provided "grateful release" from traditional functions, he will enthusiastically accept the new role. Further, some teachers are not qualified to fill the new role, and this aggravates the fear, hostility, and resistance.[22]

Chu and Schramm comment on television specifically. The first of its two chief disadvantages is that "it is essentially a one-way medium. . . . It is not a good device for classroom discussion or for giving quick answers to questions from students." A second disadvantage is the difficulty of "building television into the ongoing activities of a classroom, fitting the same material to the needs of different classes at the same time, and creating an efficient team-teaching situation where the teachers may be miles apart. And because this is difficult and sometimes threatening and aggravating to the classroom teachers, we have a history of resistance to instructional television."[23]

The third major reason that teachers resist instructional technology is the ineptitude and insensitivity of the producers, suppliers, and promoters of the things of learning. One professional engineering group notes that ". . . many attempts at the application of technology to education have been parochial and unimaginative transfers of devices from the industrial or entertainment world to the classroom. Applications have often been carried out with little concern for the psychology of the classroom teachers, often with uncertain and sometimes clearly detrimental results."[24] In the words of one critic, "The suppliers of technology have been very slow to produce genuinely useful systems at suitable prices which will add to the educational process rather than complicate it."[25]

However, OECD's Centre for Educational Research and Innovation argues that short-sighted educators are even more blameworthy:

Education, although essentially a form of communication, has been the undertaking least affected in its mode of operation by recent developments. It is not surprising, therefore, that to the majority concerned with education, educational technology implies little more than gimmickry (and expensive at that)—a fringe activity peripheral to the real task of education. One reason for this attitude may be found in the promotional methods of some producers who oversell their equipment. The main factor, however, is the failure on the part of educators to appreciate that new means of communication require a radical review of the teaching-learning process.[26]

A fourth substantial reason for teachers' resistance of the technology of instruction is that frequently they have been assigned a secondary role or no role at all in its planning and use. Not only is the teacher ignored in the planning, curriculum designing, and decision-making, but training in the use of the new media is either inadequate or non-existent. Hence, aloofness, hostility, or active opposition. The International Council for Educational Development, in a paper prepared for the Corporation for Public Broadcasting, puts it this way: "We have generally neglected to train our teachers in the use of the new media and, with other factors, this has resulted in resistance to the technology as a regular feature in many classrooms." The paper continues:

From the point of view of the good teacher, it can be said that there are three tests governing the admission of something new into the system of the individual classroom. Is it convenient to do so, or is it more trouble than it is worth? Does the content provide an element that the teacher considers indispensable, something that he cannot provide himself and that will otherwise be unavailable? Finally, what is the contribution to the effectiveness of the learning process?[27]

Yet the teachers are not completely inculpable. As one disillusioned instructional technologist has put it: "The reason so little instructional technology is used in education today is that its visible faults always end up being compared with the teacher's invisible virtues."[28]

The Hardware-Software Dichotomy

In instructional technology today there is nothing quite as pervasive as the hardware-software dichotomy. One of the more interesting educational phenomena of the '60s was the way in which the educational technology business burgeoned, skyrocketed, and subsequently plummeted. The available, lucrative market initially envisioned by the publishers, media men, and new technologists proved to be a costly illusion. In the wake of the multi-million-dollar mistake came recrimination, retrenchment, reorganization, and a new corporate caution.

As the '70s began, one major learning corporation rationalized (and wrote off) its multi-million-dollar loss of the four previous years (in new proprietary learning systems, educational services, and multi-media instructional materials) as an effort to establish a beachhead in the emerging education and training markets of the 1970s rather than in competing for existing large traditional markets now served by well-entrenched publishing firms."[29]

"We perceive our role," the president said, "as a service corporation to assist educational institutions to solve fundamental systems problems of instruction and management. . . . We are concerned with the program side—the software of education—and will develop proprietary hardware only to the minimum extent essential to solve educational problems which will not yield to existing technology."[30]

While the new objective is laudable, its economic feasibility is questionable in a business in which substantial sales volume of relatively high-cost equipment is essential to success. Although the costs of software development tend to be high, the returns tend to be low—at least when the new software is a small-scale, short-term curricular additive and not a large-scale, long-term substitute.

One of the major deterrents to the use of educational technology is, of course, the high cost of "various hardware configurations." What is needed, according to a National Academy of Engineering report, is "a low-cost, compact display unit using a low-cost recording medium usable by the average, non-technical student. . . ."[31]

Still another deterrent is the rapid rate of change that characterizes instructional technology. A current innovation may soon be obsolete. Explains the International Council for Educational Development,

Cable television, video-records, and computer-assisted instruction all foreshadow great changes that might make existing broadcast arrangements obsolete. It has thus been difficult to convince teachers and administrators to make large investments in current technology when they know very well that their new hardware may be obsolete by the end of a decade.[32]

Theoretically there is an almost unlimited hardware capability—provided the need is believed great enough, the number to be reached large enough, and hence the cost reasonable enough. The practical limitations on hardware are in the desire for it, the worth of the content to use with it, and the willingness to pay the cost involved. The willingness, of course, is related to other needs and the priorities.

The problem then becomes one of software: the substance, content, or program delivered by the system to the user. Frequently in the past both the educators and the hardware producers have looked first at the equipment available, usually developed for some other purpose, and then tried to find an educational use for it. This approach is no longer acceptable. While everyone laments the lack of usable, salable software, producing it is more difficult. James Du-Molin finds a "major deterrent" to quality software development in the "cottage industry" method of program production that currently exists: each school system, or even separate schools within a system, attempt to satisfy their own local needs.[33]

James Miller urges basic research on software technology, "including new methods of programming, creation of new programming languages, and work on basic linguistics in order to improve the ability of computers to translate text from one language to another or to search text and answer questions based on such searches."[34]

"The key to effective educational technology rests in software," concludes Eugene Cogan.[35] Without research on software, the promise of the things of learning as an aid to education will remain largely unrealized.

Individualized Multi-Media Learning

Modern pedagogical writing abounds with suggestions for the individualization of instruction. Educators and psychologists, increasingly aware of learning differences, seek to enable each child to achieve to the highest level of his ability. In the campaign for individualized instruction and individualized learning, various "things of learning" have, sequentially, been acclaimed as offering a solution to the needs for individualized instruction. After a decade of promise and trial, students, teachers, administrators, and suppliers of the things of learning tend to concur that the answer to the question "Which technology?" is "Several,"—each appropriate to a particular task.

Diebold identifies four trends which are "close to being convictions throughout broad strata of educators and a growing proportion of the public." The first of these is that "instruction must become more individualized, especially for the disadvantaged and the particularly gifted. Even the median student develops at different rates in different areas and at different times in his development. The requirement that all proceed together assures boredom in some, a sense of failure in others, and wholly fails to develop the potential of each."[36]

According to the Centre for Educational Research and Innovation eight media can assist in the individualization of learning:

> . . . print in all forms
> . . . moving visual and audio-visual media (film, television, videotape)
> . . . static visual media (slide transparencies, photographs)
> . . . sound media (tape recordings, radio, Gramophone discs)
> . . . situational information (as in drama, role playing, educational games, case studies)
> . . . information from physical objects (models, simulators)
> . . . computers (CAI, CMI)
> . . . human resources (teachers and peers)[37]

support audio

To fit the media to the purpose, ICED proposes a series of regional dissemination points called telecommunications centers; the centers would be "the source of quality units of multi-media programming" and would aim at "total exploitation" and "maximum utilization ... through all practicable learning environments and technologies."[38]

In his Japan Prize Lecture in 1969, Schramm said that two of the main currents in modern education are the new role of the teacher and the new importance of individualized instruction. He combined the two as follows:

The teacher is coming to be a kind of stage manager for a number of learning activities—television, films, books, programmed instruction, explanation, discussion, practice, experiments, individual projects, field trips, and many others. The focus has moved from the teacher teaching to the student learning: the teacher's job is to arrange a series of learning opportunities that will fit the individual student's needs and capabilities and stimulate him to learn in the only way he can learn—in his own way, at his own rate, by his own efforts.[39]

A new organizational structure is required that will not only utilize a variety of media but will make it possible to individualize teaching in a "man-machine system of instruction."[40] But both teacher and machine are essential. T.H. Bell notes that "the machine cannot recognize a puzzled expression or respond to an uplifted hand. It cannot discuss the implications for life of certain ideas or issues as they relate to a specific person. It cannot motivate and inspire on an *individualized* basis. The most *crucial* and *highly necessary* instructional duties must be performed by the teacher/professor."[41]

Daily the economic realities of education assail the American public. According to Atwater, a nation whose overburdened school system faces collapse has two alternatives: (a) either massively increase the amount of resources going into it or (b) increase its efficiency and effectiveness by "finding ways for the present schools through technology to expand the influence of a limited teacher corps and/or to improve the system of instruction by placing a heavier responsibility for education on the learner by an investment in new learning systems, materials, and technologies."[42]

While there is general agreement on the desirability, even the necessity, of multi-media usage in the solution of educational problems, the manner in which the media will be used and the changes in structure and process they will require are still open to conjecture.

Research and Evaluation

Instructional technology research and evaluation is murky terrain with few illuminating guideposts. Almost all research on instructional technology concludes that more data are needed on *this* subject; and that *additional* subjects—related, remote, or totally irrelevant—demand study.[43] The lack of conclusive research is primarily the result of five conditions:

The ambiguity of the definition of instructional technology. By attaching any of many intangible meanings to the term, almost any piece of educational research can become, and be justified as, educational or instructional technology research.

The tendency—accidental, intentional, or sometimes simply convenient—to treat instructional technology and television as synonymous. Most of the research reports in the literature deal with television; and most of the data on which they are based are at least six years old.

The repeated inconclusiveness and tentativeness of the findings. The research designs, the caution and the evasive language that surround much educational research all contribute to this uncertainty. As repeated research in the teaching uses of television in the '60s monotonously concluded: "No significant difference." Or, as Morrison succinctly puts it: "When everything is as good as, nothing is better than."[44]

The fragmentation of the research. This fragmented nature renders findings inapplicable to other situations and virtually useless as a source of valid information.

Different interpretations of the same research. A project considered successful by some writers may be considered a failure by others. In general, the closer to the project, the more favorably one is likely to view it.

Locke and Engler decry the focus of research on the medium—student-teacher ratios and relative costs of capital equipment as compared with salaries—rather than on the process of learning:

Enormous amounts of money have been spent on instructional television without (as yet) any really satisfactory judgments about its value. ... Very little of the analysis of ITV has been in terms of how well it can be adapted to an instructional strategy that takes into account the differences in learning style and rate.[45]

Although general research on learning is needed, specific research on instructional technology also is needed to produce better results.

Such research would involve more modest, clearly stated objectives, focused on measurable performance by a specific medium over a pre-determined time span, under manageable circumstances, with realistic amounts of money, indigenously supplied. In this instance, "better" results would be those applicable immediately, without fanfare and especially without large infusions of additional funds, to change and improve education.

Effective, conclusive research and evaluation are essential to the future of instructional technology. Not only do they further the state of knowledge, but the findings, if positive, will become the most persuasive advocate for the application of the things of learning.

Notes

1. Sidney G. Tickton, (ed.) *To Improve Learning—An Evaluation of Instructional Technology, Vol. I,* New York and London, R.R. Bowker Company, 1971, p. 32.

2. Hilliard Jason, "Instructional Technology in Medical Education," in Sidney G. Tickton (ed.) *To Improve Learning, Vol. II,* New York and London, R. R. Bowker Company, 1971, p. 740.

3. Norman MacKenzie, Michael Eraut and Hywel C. Jones, *Teaching and Learning: An Introduction to New Methods and Resources in Higher Education,* UNESCO and the International Association of Universities, Paris, 1970, p. 93.

4. Harold Gores, Interview July 13, 1971.

5. *New Educational Media in Action: Case Studies for Planners—II,* UNESCO, International Institute for Educational Planning, Paris, 1967, p. 13.

6. Henri Dieuzeide, "Educational Technology: Sophisticated, Adapted and Rational Technology," Series B: Opinions No. 30, International Commission on the Development of Education, UNESCO, 1970, p. 3.

7. Henri Dieuzeide, "Educational Technology and Development of Education," International Education Year 1970, UNESCO, Paris, Document No. 8 of a series of 12, p. 7.

8. Sidney G. Tickton, (ed.) *To Improve Learning—An Evaluation of Instructional Technology, Vol. I,* New York and London, R. R. Bowker Company, 1970, p. 88.

9. David Engler, "Independent Learning Systems—Their Production and International Transfer," Background paper for conference, Dublin; Ireland, September 1970, Paris, OECD/CERI, August 1971, p. 4.

10. Robert W. Locke, "Has the American Education Industry Lost its Nerve?" *Journal of Educational Technology, No. 2, Vol. I,* May 1970, p. 112.

11. Robert J. Blakely, "Shaping the Future," *Educational Broadcasting Review, Vol. V,* No. 3, p. 4.

12. Kenneth A. Christiansen, Interview August 6, 1971.

13. Anthony G. Oettinger, *Run, Computer Run,* Cambridge, Mass., Harvard University Press, 1969, p. 110, 111.

14. Quoted in Robert H. Anderson, "Organizational and Administrative Changes Needed in Schools and Colleges in Order for New Techniques to Effectively Improve Instruction," in Sidney G. Tickton, (ed.) *To Improve Learning Vol. II,* New York and London, R. R. Bowker Company, 1971, p. 413.

15. Dave Berkman, "The Learning Industry and ITV," *Educational Broadcasting Review, Vol. V,* No. 3, June 1971, p. 24.

16. Hugh Beckwith, "Innovations in Industry Likely to Affect Instructional Technology During the Next Ten Years," in Sidney G. Tickton, (ed.) *To Improve Learning Vol. II*, New York and London, R. R. Bowker Company, 1971, p. 853.

17. Dave Berkman, "The Learning Industry and ITV," *Educational Broadcasting Review, Vol. V*, No. 3, June 1971, p. 24.

18. John Diebold, *Education, Technology and Business*, Praeger Publishers, Inc., New York, 1971, p. 30.

19. James R. DuMolin, "Instructional Television Utilization in the United States," Memorandum No. 71-6, St. Louis, Washington University, October 1971, p. 34.

20. Bernard Trotter, *Television and Technology in University Teaching*, A Report to the Committee on University Affairs, and the Committee of Presidents of Universities of Ontario, published by the Committee on University Affairs and the Committee of Presidents of Universities of Ontario, Toronto, 1970, p. 16.

21. Alva R. Dittrick, "Developing Relevant Education Through Instructional Technology," in Sidney G. Tickton (ed.) *To Improve Learning Vol. II*, New York and London, R. R. Bowker Company, 1971, p. 572.

22. Dave Berkman, "The Learning Industry and ITV," *Educational Broadcasting Review, Vol. V*, No. 3, June 1971, p. 24.

23. Godwin C. Chu and Wilbur Schramm, *Learning from Television, What the Research Says*, National Association of Educational Broadcasters, Washington, D. C., 1967, pp. 100-101.

24. "Educational Technology in Higher Education: The Promises and Limitations of ITV and CAI," Instructional Technology Committee of the Commission on Education of the National Academy of Engineering, Washington, D. C., September 1969, p. 1.

25. Frank J. Doyle and Daniel Z. Goodwill, *An Exploration of the Future in Educational Technology*, Bell Canada, 1971, p. 1.

26. Educational Technology, *The Design and Implementation of Learning Systems*, Report based on the results of a workshop organized by CERI in conjunction with the British, Dutch, German and Swedish Authorities at Leiden, Netherlands, April 1970, OECD, 1970, p. 11.

27. "Instructional Broadcasting: A Design for the Future," A paper prepared for the Corporation for Public Broadcasting by the International Council for Educational Development, January 15, 1971, p. 5.

28. Hugh Beckwith, "Innovations in Industry Likely to Affect Instructional Technology During the Next Ten Years," in Sidney G. Tickton (ed.) *To Improve Learning Vol. II*, New York and London, R. R. Bowker Company, 1971, p. 851.

29. Verne S. Atwater, "The Changing Educational Marketplace, A Nontraditional Approach," Paper presented at Financial Analysts Federation 1970 Fall Conference, Rochester, New York, October 1970.

30. *Ibid.*

31. "Educational Technology in Higher Education: The Promises and Limitations of ITV and CAI," Instructional Technology Committee of the Commission on Education of the National Academy of Engineering, Washington, D. C., September 1969, p. 4.

32. "Instructional Broadcasting: A Design for the Future," Paper prepared for the Corporation for Public Broadcasting by the International Council for Educational Development, January 15, 1971, p. 7.

33. James R. DuMolin, "Instructional Television Utilization in the United States," Memorandum No. 71-6, St. Louis, Washington University, October 1970, p. 19.

34. James G. Miller, "A Ten Year Program for Developing, Evaluating and Implementing Instructional Technology," in Sidney G. Tickton (ed.) *To Improve Learning Vol. II*, New York and London, R. R. Bowker Company, 1971, p. 274.

35. Eugene A. Cogan, "Systems Analysis and the Introduction of Educational

Technology in Schools," in Sidney G. Tickton (ed.) *To Improve Learning Vol. II,* New York and London, R. R. Bowker Company, 1971, p. 36.

36. John Diebold, *Education, Technology and Business,* Praeger Publishers, Inc., New York, 1971, p. 3. The other three are: (a) public education must begin earlier; (b) education must continue longer; and (c) the public deserves more options in education than are presently available.

37. *Educational Technology, The Design and Implementation of Learning Systems,* Report based on the results of a workshop organized by CERI in conjunction with the British, Dutch, German, and Swedish Authorities at Leiden, Netherlands, April 1970, OECD, 1970, p. 25.

38. *Instructional Broadcasting: A Design for the Future,* A paper prepared for the Corporation for Public Broadcasting by the International Council for Educational Development, January 15, 1971, p. 28.

39. Wilbur Schramm, "The Future of Educational Radio and Television," *Japan Prize Lecture,* November, 1969, p. 11.

40. T. H. Bell, "Implications of the New Technologies for School and College Organization and Administration," in Sidney G. Tickton, (ed.) *To Improve Learning Vol. II,* New York and London, R. R. Bowker Company, 1971, p. 427.

41. *Ibid.,* p. 429.

42. Verne S. Atwater, "Results to be Expected from Private Enterprise Investment in Education," Remarks at the Institute of International Education Conference, San Francisco, October 31, 1969, p. 10.

43. The research findings are not reviewed in this section. They mostly are in television, as we have indicated. The best summary was prepared by Chu and Schramm for the National Association of Educational Broadcasters in 1967 and later summarized in the Commission on Instructional Technology report.

44. W. Earl Morrison, Interview January 31, 1972.

45. Robert W. Locke and David Engler, "Instructional Technology: The Capabilities of Industry to Help Solve Educational Problems," in Sidney G. Tickton (ed.) *To Improve Learning Vol. II,* New York and London, R. R. Bowker Company, 1971, p. 916.

CHAPTER THREE

The Things of Learning

The "things of learning" that have the potential to make a significant quantitative or qualitative difference in education are: television (and television-related technologies), film, audio tape, radio, programmed instruction and means for its presentation, computers, and books.

This chapter is an examination of what and how each of these things can contribute to the processes of learning and education. For each, the physical functioning of the technology is described, a review is made of past effectiveness in furthering learning and education, and suggestions are made as to what are likely to be productive uses of the technology and what are some operational problems which might be encountered. There is no attempt to estimate costs. Cost considerations are important but, as will become evident, little is known with certainty about either relative educational effectiveness or operational costs of the different technologies. The one indisputable statement which can be made about costs is that there has been consistent underestimate of what it takes to produce effective educational programs—not only in money, but in human skills, testing and revision, and time.

Television

Basic Television Technology

The picture on the screen of a television tube is generated by the emission of light of varying intensity from roughly 200,000 points on the screen, these being arranged in a series of 525 horizontal lines.[1] The light comes from a fluorescent material on the inner face of the screen, the material at each point emitting light in proportion to the intensity of an electron beam which sweeps sequentially across all the horizontal lines to produce a complete picture change every 1/30 of a second, i.e., at the rate of 30 "frames" per second. The glow of the fluorescent material at each point decreases rapidly after the electron beam passes so if the same picture is to be maintained the screen will have to be "refreshed" by the electron beam every 1/30 of a second.

In the normal use of television, the signal which ultimately is displayed on the face of the television set is generated by an electronic camera in the television studio. Such cameras are capable of scanning each 1/30th of a second some 200,000 discrete points in its field of view and associating with each point the intensity of light coinciding with that point. This information is processed electrically by equipment in the transmitting station and delivered via radio waves to the home receiver, there to be processed into the form needed to drive an electron gun which sweeps the electron beam across the horizontal lines on the screen of the television tube.

It may be seen that the amount of electrical information which must be transmitted each second to generate pictures on the face of the television tube must be of the order of (30 frames per second) x (200,000 points per frame) or 6,000,000 variations per second. In contrast, the audio part of the television signal requires transmittal of only about one thousandth of this electrical information since most transmitted television sounds are in the frequency range of 7,000 cycles per second or less.

The term "bandwidth" is used to describe the electrical information content of a given signal; for example, the bandwidth of the television audio signal is said to be only about one thousandth the bandwidth of the picture signal. One result of this very high information content of the television picture signal is that a telephone line which has the electrical capacity to transmit voice with high quality is physically incapable of transmitting the information required for a television picture; it does not have the required bandwidth capacity. Thus, when the television signal must be transmitted by means other than direct radio wave broadcast, it is necessary to employ special "broadband" techniques such as microwave line-of-sight transmission networks or special cable which connects the receiver to the transmitting station.

Color television equipment is more complex and delicate than black and white, although advances in solid state electronic technology give promise to reduce its costs and to increase its ruggedness and dependability. The inner face of the screen of the color television tube is covered with some 200,000 clusters of three different fluorescent phosphors, each emitting a different color of light (red, green or blue) when excited by an electron beam. An electron beam sweeps across the horizontal lines in the same manner as in the black and white tube, but with intensity and position controls such that the emitted light from the three phosphor dots combine to produce the proper color and brightness required at each point. In the color television studio the electronic camera is constructed such that the light incident upon the camera is analyzed optically and electronically and electrical signals are generated proportional to its content of red, green and blue light. These three color signals are combined electronically into a brightness or luminance signal and into a color or chrominance signal, both of which are transmitted by radio waves over a single television channel to the home receivers, and there decoded into the signals for the electron gun in the picture tube.

In addition to transmitting live broadcasts, the standard television station has equipment for recording and playback on magnetic (video) tape, for recording television pictures on film (kinescope), and for converting movie film, mostly 16 mm, to television signals for broadcast. From the production standpoint, videotape and film have been quite distinct mediums because of differences in the technical capabilities of the equipment available. In film production most of the shooting is done with a single camera with optimum lighting and camera position for each shot, and the film is put together later in the editing room with use of the Moviola editing machine. In contrast, because of the lack of equipment which will allow electronic editing of videotape with the facility with which film can be edited on the Moviola, most videotape production has been done with multiple cameras and real time editing, i.e., with the director switching from one camera to another to record at any instant the camera view he prefers, and with only limited editing being done subsequent to recorded shooting.

However, current developments in electronic editing indicate that videotape may soon be edited as easily as film is edited on the Moviola. These developments and the recent introduction of smaller, more portable television cameras and portable broadcast-quality videotape recorders auger more flexible and mobile videotape production. Within the next few years, videotape will possess the flexibility and mobility of current film production, in addition to its present capability of production with multiple cameras and real time editing. Then the choice between videotape and film will depend upon other factors such as relative costs, availability of equipment and facilities, preferences of producer and director, number of reproductions required, type of display equipment available at use points, etc.

Related Television Technology

The following devices and processes have been, or are being, developed to improve or augment some aspect of either the program storage or the transmission flexibility and capability of the basic television technology.

RECORDING AND PLAYBACK SYSTEMS

During the past few years several of the major manufacturers of consumer electronic equipment have been attempting to develop systems capable of playing recorded programs through a standard television receiver. They envisioned these playback-recording systems as potentially large-volume consumer electronic products which would produce sales to counteract the growing saturation of the home television market. Since the field was new, many of the systems were dissimilar or incompatible; each manufacturer hoped that his system would prove to be superior and become "standard" for the industry. With the exception of reel-to-reel magnetic videotape machines, all systems which are now being actively marketed or for which marketing plans have been announced employ a form of cartridge which the user merely inserts into the playback machine.

MAGNETIC VIDEOTAPE

Reel-to-Reel. The recording of television programs on magnetic tape began in 1956 with the introduction of broadcast quality equipment using 2-inch tape on which the information for successive frames was recorded in a direction perpendicular to the tape, i.e., in the 2-inch direction as the tape moved through the recorder. This configuration of equipment was further developed over the years to incorporate the color capability now a part of broadcast recorders.

In the early 1960's black and white portable recorders were developed using less costly 1-inch, and subsequently 1/2-inch, magnetic tape on which the television information was recorded in a diagonal direction intermediate between the perpendicular and longitudinal directions: so-called helical scan videotape recorders. Initially these recorders were not of broadcast station quality, transmitted solely in black and white, and were used mainly by other than broadcasters for recording of broadcasts for subsequent replay through a standard television receiver or, in concert with compact and lightweight cameras, for making television programs for educational, industrial or commercial use. However, there is now on the market a 1-inch helical scan color recorder guaranteed to have broadcast quality.

A large number of these reel-to-reel machines have been sold; approximately 25 percent of U.S. public schools have such a videotape recorder, most purchased under federal aid programs.[2]

Cassette Loading.   As of this writing, two helical scan cartridge-loading videotape systems are being marketed in the U.S., both with color capability. The Sony "U-Matic" videocassette system uses 3/4-inch magnetic tape running at 3.75 inches per second in a cassette which has two reels arranged as in the ubiquitous Philips audio cassette. This cassette can hold up to 1,200 feet of tape, enough for 60 minutes of showing; rewinding takes about 3 minutes. Sony is offering both a player model (which is connected to the antenna terminals of a television receiver) and a player-recorder model which has capability for recording from a camera or from a broadcast or cable transmission.

Sony is quoting retail prices of approximately $1,000 for the player and $1,400 for the player-recorder. Individual unrecorded cassettes are quoted at prices ranging from under $25, when loaded with tape for a 30-minute show, to under $40 for 60 minutes. These prices for equipment, cassettes, and recording will come down as the market volume increases. Sony marketing plans provide that cassette sales to high volume users will be through joint venture companies specializing in magnetic tape duplication and using special machines developed by Sony. Four other manufacturers have made arrangements with Sony to manufacture its U-Matic videocassette or a compatible system: Matsushita Electric (Panasonic), Japan Victor, 3M Company (Wollensak) and Philips (Norelco). None of these has announced marketing plans or quoted prices for U.S. delivery.

Although several U.S. manufacturers are working on videotape cassettes, the only other videotape cartridge system now being offered for sale in the U.S. is the Cartrivision system of Cartridge Television, Inc., a division of the Avco Corporation. The Cartrivision system runs at essentially the same speed as Sony (3.8 as against 3.75 inches per second) but utilizes only 1/2-inch tape as contrasted with Sony's 3/4-inch. This saving in tape is achieved by making use of the fact that the television picture or "frame" is changed in two steps, the "field" of even numbered horizontal lines being changed during the first 1/60th of a second and the field of odd numbered lines being changed in the second 1/60th of a second. In the Cartrivision system every third field is recorded, i.e., 20 fields per second, and then each recorded field is played back three times. This procedure results in some degradation of the image when rapid motion takes place, but most observers have not found this troublesome. Cartrivision offers two cassettes, each having two reels that are mounted coaxially, one on top of the other. One cassette can hold up to 570 feet of tape, enough for 30 minutes of showing; the other cassette can hold up to 2,170 feet of tape, enough for 114 minutes of showing. Cartrivision will manufacture cassettes and will be actively involved in cassette marketing. It plans to concentrate, at the outset, on the consumer market and experiment with different sales and rental schemes for recorded cassettes; it has acquired the rights to over 200 feature-length programs which it will offer in recorded cassettes. The basic recording and playback equipment is manufactured by Cartrivision and sold to television manufacturers who incorporate these into products with their own television receivers and market them under their brand names.

The price at which Cartrivision is offering the basic recording and playback unit to manufacturers is not available. Based on announced prices of manufacturer's television receivers incorporating the unit, this price probably will be approximately $300 or less. Prices for cassettes of different program length and different number of duplication also are not generally available but, as an example, Cartrivision has indicated that 1000 cassettes recorded with 30 minutes of material supplied by the customer would cost under $20 each.

In Europe, the Philips Company has developed and begun marketing of its Video Cassette Recorder (VCR) system which uses 1/2-inch tape running at 6.75 inches per second in a cassette of the same general design as that of Cartrivision. A number of major European television receiver manufacturers have made licensing arrangements for producing VCR player-recorders. Introduction into the U.S. will require technical changes to achieve compatibility with U.S. television, and Philips (Norelco) has not announced plans to enter the U.S. market with this system. Several Japanese manufacturers are reported to have agreed on common standards for 1/2-inch videotape cassettes, but no products built to these standards are yet on the market.

The field of magnetic videotape cassettes will remain tumultuous until a consensus on standards evolves. Possibly new systems will be introduced which use substantially less tape through much denser storage of information, a density achieved through improved recording heads or better magnetic tapes.

Because they combine the electronic complexity of color television with the electro-mechanical complications of very high quality and high precision audio cassette tape recorders, the video tape cassette recorder players are more complicated than any consumer equipment yet marketed by the electronics industry. As a consequence, only experience will reveal what will be the problems of machine maintenance and durability of these machines when they are in the hands of the public.

ELECTRONIC VIDEO RECORDING (EVR)

EVR is a system developed by CBS in which motion pictures and television programs are recorded on photographic film; the film subsequently is used in an EVR player to recreate the program on the screen of a standard television receiver. The system uses black and white film 8.75 mm wide which has on it two tracks of images, ten images per inch, and two magnetic stripe audio tracks, one on each edge of the film. When the program is in black and white each track of images stores half the program and there is a program interruption between the two halves while the film is rewound. When the program is in color one track of images carries the brightness (luminance) information and the other track the color (chrominance) information, with the result that the same length of film carries half as much color program as black and white program.

The film is packaged in a circular cassette which can hold up to 750 feet of film, enough for 25 minutes of color program. When the cassette is inserted in the player, the end of the film automatically is grasped and guided through the player to a take-up reel. Inside the player the film emulsion density at each point is measured with a

light beam and a photocell and the resulting information is processed electronically and fed to the antenna terminals of the television receiver. After showing, the film automatically is rewound into
the cartridge.

The production of copies of EVR film employs standard movie
film production techniques and equipment. However, the close tol-
erances required on image sharpness and emulsion density have necessitated development of new equipment for generating the mas-
ter prints from which the copies are made.

These requirements suggest that EVR will be restricted to the
relatively high volume market, with all EVR films being made in a
few production centers. CBS has licensed a number of manufacturers to make EVR players; Motorola began production in 1970 and
has been selling them for around $800. CBS retained for itself the
rights to manufacture EVR films and cassettes in the U.S. and established a production center in New Jersey. However, in December,
1971, CBS announced the closing of its New Jersey production center and its withdrawal from further involvement with EVR except
through its investment in the EVR Partnership with Imperial
Chemical Industries Ltd. and CIBA Ltd. The Partnership was
formed in 1968 to establish an English production center for films and
cassettes. It is not known whether CBS's withdrawal was the result
of technical problems with the EVR system, of marketing problems, or of financial problems. It is not yet clear whether or under
what arrangements the EVR Partnership and the manufacturers
who have committed themselves to EVR player production will
continue to make EVR available.

SELECTA VISION

In 1969 RCA announced it was developing a video cassette system
which would record television programs in the form of holographic
patterns embossed on inexpensive plastic tape. The inexpensive
tape would be complemented by high speed, and therefore low
cost, embossing techniques. It was predicted that this combination
would lead to recorded cassettes whose price, exclusive of program
material costs, would be very low, perhaps only one-fourth that of
comparable cassettes in the EVR format. Like EVR, the Selecta-
Vision system was aimed at the presumed large market for prerecorded programs. Within the SelectaVision player a laser beam is
passed through the holographic impression embossed on the plastic
tape, and in so doing reconstructs and projects outward from the

tape the original television image. This image is focussed on the face of an electronic camera whose output is electronically converted and fed to the antenna terminals of a television receiver.

In late 1969, a laboratory black and white version of this system demonstrated television pictures of marginal acceptability. RCA is reported subsequently to have improved the television images of a prototype black and white version to acceptable quality and to have made substantial progress on the color version. At the same time RCA has made no announcements about definite marketing plans, and this has led to speculation that RCA may be having trouble with development of the production version of the system. Such a situation would not be surprising since RCA chose to combine in this system several relatively complicated processes, none of which had been employed in a mass produced consumer product. Prior to the decision of CBS to withdraw from the prerecorded program approach to the video cassette market, RCA was known to be carrying out development work on a videotape cassette system which also would be marketed under the trade name of SelectaVision. It is unlikely, however, that it will depart widely from other videotape cassette systems and thus will not offer to users any substantially different alternative as would the holographic system.

Video Disc

Teldec, a joint venture of A.E.G. Telefunken and British Decca, has developed the video disc. Similar to a phonograph record, the video disc has grooves formed on its surface and is played on a machine which looks like a record player. However, the information is stored on the video disc in a fundamentally different form which allows the very dense storage of information needed for the television picture. On the video disc the information is recorded in minute vertical, rather than sidewise, deviations in the depth of the grooves, thus allowing adjacent grooves to be spaced about fifteen times closer together than on an LP record. By combining this higher groove density with both a rotational speed of 1,500 rpm and a new pickup system which allows very close spacing of depth variations along each groove, Teldec has been able to develop video discs which record approximately 7 minutes of black and white television on 8-inch diameter discs and up to 15 minutes on 12-inch discs. The quality of picture is said by observers to be not up to broadcast standards but completely adequate for home or normal educational use.

Because the discs can be manufactured of relatively low cost material by record pressing techniques, the video disc system has the potential for drastically reducing the price of programs if they are required in large enough quantities to justify the preparation of the masters needed for pressing. In order to realize this potential, Teldec will need an automatic changer which will accept cassettes containing discs for up to 60 minutes of program and will require only very brief program interruptions between discs. Teldec has announced that production players and player-changers employing 5 minute color discs will be available in early 1973. Prices of approximately $250 for the player and $400 for the player-changer have been announced. Prices for discs will depend on software costs and the number to be pressed, but Teldec has mentioned prices in the range of $2.50 to $4.00.

The mechanical mechanism and pickup of the Teldec player appears to be simpler and less subject to wear than that of videotape players and thus may require less maintenance. It may also require less storage space for recorded programs; the actual advantage will depend on how little the volume of the disc cassette proves to exceed the volume of the discs contained within it.

Video disc systems are known to be under development by several companies. Philips recently demonstrated a laboratory model of a system in which the video information is stored in the form of tiny pits and recovered by variations in the intensity of a narrow laser beam of light reflected from the pits as the disc rotates at high speed. The lack of direct recording capability will relegate video disc systems to the high volume market, but within this market they will have a clear price advantage over videotape systems.

Super 8 Film

Several companies have Super 8 film videoplayers under development, and some have demonstrated systems. In 1970, Vidicord Holdings Ltd. began marketing a black and white manual threading videoplayer in England. In the fall of 1971, Kodak demonstrated a color automatic threading videoplayer but announced no marketing plans. Kodak used in its demonstration model the same Super 8 film cartridge used in its Super 8 optical projector. Kodak has offered this cartridge to other projector manufacturers on a very easy licensing arrangement, in the hopes that it will become a standard for the industry. This cartridge contains a single reel which will hold up to about 30 minutes of magnetic sound film; the end of the film is grasped and threaded automatically through to a take-up reel within the projector when the cartridge is inserted; at the conclusion, the film automatically is rewound into the cartridge. Within the player a light beam and three photocells measure the intensities of red, green and blue color at each point of the image and this information is converted electronically into luminance and chrominance signals to be fed to the antenna terminals of a television receiver.

A Super 8 videoplayer would permit projection of a program either through a television screen to a small group or through an optical projector to a large audience. It also would provide easy television access to the library of Super 8 film already available and to additional ones produced in the future. However, the player would not provide local recording capability. Since the Super 8 videoplayer would be similar in operation to the EVR player, its manufacturing cost probably would be comparable. The prices of Super 8 recorded cartridges are likely to be close to those of EVR cassettes for the same lengths of programs, the cheaper material costs for the black and white EVR film being counterbalanced by somewhat lower processing costs for duplicating the Super 8. Kodak probably will market a Super 8 videoplayer and license other manufacturers in order to encourage wider use of Super 8 film. Such players probably will not be available until 1973 or 1974.

CABLE TRANSMISSION

A television cable is an alternative transmission system to over-the-air radio wave broadcasting of television signals. However, cable transmission also offers channel capacities and other capabilities not available in radiated transmission. Although within the radiated electromagnetic frequency spectrum there are 12 television channels allocated in the very high frequency (VHF) band and 70 in the ultra high frequency (UHF) band, as a result of interference between channels which are adjacent in the frequency spectrum or between stations using the same channel in nearby locations and because of technical and economic difficulties encountered in developing the UHF band the average number of channels actually available in 86 of the 100 largest markets in the U.S. is only 3.4. In contrast, a single television cable system has the capacity to transmit simultaneously at least twenty channels with a relatively modest equipment investment, and can carry perhaps as many as forty channels by use of more sophisticated, and more expensive, equipment. Further, unlike the over-the-air transmission, the signals within the cable are not influenced by external conditions, and there is no interference between signals. Thus a cable can deliver good pictures in a city environment where reception of broadcast signals may be hampered by reflections and obstructions.

This channel capacity is made possible by the electrical properties of the coaxial cable, consisting of two concentric conductors, that is used for transmission. This concentric positioning of the two conductors permits such a cable to transmit electrical signals of very high frequency and over a wide bandwidth. The coaxial cable used for television is designed to transmit all frequencies between about 40 million and 300 million cycles per second, a region of the frequency spectrum which includes all of the VHF channels and the FM radio spectrum band but does not include any of the UHF broadcast band.

An installed cable system is schematically analogous to a tree in that from the signal source, usually called the "head end," a trunk cable runs out through the area to be served, and from this branch out feeder lines to which individual users are connected by so-called drop lines. Other electronic circuitry can be installed along the cable to accomplish specific purposes; two examples of circuitry are special filters which deny an individual user access to one or more channels and equipment which makes it possible for an individual user to send a signal to the head-end, i.e., to have two-way communication. Undoubtedly much new technology will be developed to exploit the cable system for new uses. One such technology which already has appeared is the TICCIT (time-shared, interactive, computer-controlled, information television) system developed by the MITRE Corporation.

The TICCIT system is designed to give a large number of users of a cable television system simultaneous but individual access to a computer or other information source. The ability of the TICCIT system to serve a large number of users simultaneously is achieved at the expense of a delay in the system response time when all subscribers are, in fact, using the system at the same time. In addition to a television receiver, each subscriber in the TICCIT system has three pieces of equipment (which could be combined into one package): a coupler/decoder which is keyed to operate only with a specific code number assigned to the subscriber; a video "refresh" device; and a keyboard for communicating to a computer at the head end of the cable system.

To gain access to the system, a subscriber uses his keyboard to request TICCIT service and at the same time transmits his code number. A the head end the TICCIT television transmitter, in response to instructions received from the computer, transmits different patterns of information on each succeeding "field" and incorporates on a specific line in each field the code number of the subscriber requesting information contained in the next-following field. At the subscriber's station the coupler/decoder scans the code numbers of all incoming fields; when it encounters its own number it electronically switches the video refresh device to the record mode and couples it to the coaxial cable, and this device records the next following field. After recording this field the video refresh device automatically is switched to the playback mode; it continues to play back this field to the television receiver 30 times a second until a new field is recorded as a result of further interaction with the computer by the subscriber. Since 60 fields are transmitted per second, it may be seen that if subscribers are to wait on the average of one second for the computer response to appear on their television screen then (assuming the computer response itself is immediate) 60 subscribers could be served on one television channel. With an average response time of 10 seconds, the number of possible users goes up to 600 for one channel and up to 12,000 for a twenty channel cable. The actual response of the system would be faster since not all subscribers would be using the system at any one instant. The feasibility of the TICCIT system has been shown in a demonstration using the cable system in Reston, Virginia. The National Science Foundation has given the MITRE Corporation support to develop the TICCIT system further and experiment with its use in teaching programs, developed in cooperation with Brigham Young University, for junior colleges.

SATELLITE TRANSMISSION

Transmission of television signals from one point on the earth to another point via satellites is an everyday occurrence. As of February, 1972, six INTELSAT satellites were in service, all in geostationary synchronous orbit in locations 22,300 miles above the earth in the equatorial plane. One INTELSAT III with a capacity of 1200 telephone circuits, or four television channels, and one INTELSAT IV with a capacity of up to 9000 telephone circuits, or 12 television channels, were in orbit over the Pacific Ocean. One INTELSAT III and two INTELSAT IV's were in orbit over the Atlantic Ocean. One INTELSAT III was in orbit over the Indian Ocean. By the end of 1974, more than 80 earth station antennas are expected to be in operation in some 60 member countries of the INTELSAT consortium. The INTELSAT satellites have relatively low power transmitters. Thus the signals reaching the ground are very weak, necessitating elaborate ground receivers for signal detection and amplification. The costs of ground stations have varied from $500,000 to $2,500,000, according to the density of traffic to be carried. The INTELSAT IV series of satellites, launched during the 1970s, has more radiating power than INTELSAT III and employs antennas which can either spread the radiated energy over a wide geographical area, as the earlier INTELSAT satellites do, or focus the energy on a smaller area. The combination of higher power and antenna focussing will allow future earth receiving stations to be less elaborate and expensive and permit some flexibility in delivering the signal to only selected earth receiving stations.

The INTELSAT earth receiving stations route the satellite television signals into the local broadcast system for distribution to television receivers in the standard manner. Experiments are scheduled in the next few years to explore alternative technology for delivering satellite signals to television receivers. These experiments will be conducted as part of the NASA Applications Technology Satellite (ATS) program. In 1973 NASA plans to launch the ATS-F satellite and put it in geostationary synchronous orbit in the equatorial plane—roughly over the Galapagos Islands in the Pacific Ocean. Among the twenty-four experiments planned for the ATS-F satellite will be two technology experiments related to satellite transmission of television. One experiment will test the capability to deploy a larger and more efficient transmitting antenna than any used on INTELSAT satellites, and the other will test the accuracy of a new system for pointing the antenna at a predetermined spot on earth. These two on-board experiments are part of a NASA program to develop satellite television transmission systems which, because of more sophisticated technology in the satellite, permit much simpler ground receiving stations. If the ATS-F satellite successfully passes both of these tests, the signal strengh reaching the earth will be about fifty times stronger than that from INTELSAT IV.

In conjunction with these on-board experiments, the ATS-F satellite also will be used in overall tests of a television transmission system in which television signals received from a ground station in the U.S. will be radiated back to ground stations in the Rocky Mountain area and in Alaska. The satellite transmission will be in the newly allocated instructional TV broadcast band at 2,500 megahertz.[4] Some of the ground receivers will be very low cost and mobile installations, consisting only of a small antenna and the electronic circuitry required to process the received signals and feed one television receiver. The primary technical questions to be answered in this system test concern the quality of picture displayed on the receivers attached to the low-cost receiving stations. On-site performance of these low cost stations will depend not only on how well the ATS-F performs but also on the propagation conditions which actually exist during the tests, and on the quality of maintenance of the ground stations themselves.

The television programs beamed from the ATS-F will be primarily educational, and, concurrent with the technical experiments, there will be educational experimentation with television programs devised specially for this purpose. Some preliminary discussion has taken place concerning the carrying out of educational television and radio broadcasting experiments with Brazil during this same period.

In 1974, the ATS-F satellite is scheduled to be moved to a geostationary orbit position above Kenya in East Africa, where it will remain for a year. During this period the ATS-F will be used in an overall system experiment similar to that in which it participated while in orbit off Ecuador. Signals in the 860 megahertz frequency range, received from a transmitting station in Ahmedabad, India, will be radiated back to ground stations in India. The ground stations in India also will be of two types: relatively elaborate stations whose output will be fed to a television broadcast station and low cost stations feeding one television set. As in the Rocky Mountain and Alaska experiment, the primary technical questions relate to the quality of the pictures on television receivers fed by the low-cost stations. In this instance, however, there will be technical questions to be answered about the television receivers as well as the low-cost receiving stations. India will build both of these, primarily with indigenous parts, and thus in a sense will experiment with production of a new line of television receivers concurrently with the satellite transmission experiment.

The programs transmitted by India during this year will be aimed at one or more of the following instructional objectives: family planning, teacher training, improvement of occupational skills, agricultural practices, health and hygiene, and national integration. The low-cost receiving stations will be placed in some 2,000 villages.

Another 3,000 conventional TV receivers placed in villages will receive their satellite transmissions via three or more of the large ground receiving and rebroadcasting stations. The objective of placing the receivers in villages is so that the year's experiment can be evaluated in terms of what can be done via television to improve the conditions of the bulk of India's population, who live in its 600,000 villages.

SLOW-SCAN TELEVISION

The information transmission capacity of a voice-grade telephone line is only about one thousandth of the capacity needed for transmission of normal television (which operates at the rate of 30 complete picture changes per second). On the other hand, if one complete picture change per minute would suffice, a voice-grade telephone line would have the capacity to transmit the required picture information. In essence, this means that over a voice-grade telephone line, television could be used as a slide projector, at the rate of about one slide per minute and with a resolution comparable to that of normal television. Equipment for carrying out this process, called "slow-scan television," has been developed and is now on the market.

At the signal-generating location there is needed an electronic device which will accept standard television signals and convert these (in a process called bandwidth compression) into a form suitable for telephone line transmission. At the receiving location there must be another electronic device which reconverts the slow-scan signals to standard television signals, ready to be supplied to a television receiver. Pictures can be transmitted more rapidly than one per minute by selecting only a part of the picture information for transmission, i.e., by sacrificing resolution of the transmitted picture.

Television and Education

Much of the research done on the contribution of television to learning has been concerned with establishing the effectiveness of television relative to some other method of instruction for various subjects at different educational levels. In most of these studies, the examination performance of students who use television is compared with the performance of students who are taught face-to-face by a teacher. Some other studies have evaluated the effectiveness of instructional television on the basis of student performance on nationally administered standardized tests. The great majority of these comparisons have revealed "no significant differences" in measured learning between the television students and those instructed face-to-face.[5]

However, where these studies have revealed a statistically significant difference in effectiveness, it has been slightly more frequently in favor of television. In view of the complexity of the phenomena being measured by a single overall comparative index,[6] this difference in frequency can be taken as little more than a hopeful sign about the possible relative effectiveness of television when used well. But much of the research was conducted before 1965. In the most recently published research summary,[7] only 30 out of 305 references cover research reported after 1965. A survey of more recent research might reveal better designed experiments which would allow more definite conclusions to be drawn.

In addition to these results from comparative studies, there is a good deal of relevant information available from other sources. This information also gives support, in a more subjective but nonetheless cumulatively impressive manner, to the view that both children and adults can learn effectively from television. Some of this information is derived from research on the effects of variations in the methods of presentation and structuring of the television program; some from variations in the manner in which the program is used in the classroom. Other information is available from new methods and structuring in large scale production efforts, of which "Sesame Street" and "The Electric Company" are prime examples. A series of 23 case studies of major uses of instructional television in 18 countries has provided another range of experience and information.[8] The most recent overall evaluation of the evidence is that published in 1968 by Chu and Schramm: "Learning From Television—What the Research Says." Chu and Schramm conclude:

For one thing, it has become clear that there is no longer any reason to raise the question whether instructional television can serve as an efficient tool of learning. . . . The questions worth asking are no longer whether students learn from it, but rather (1) does the situation call for it? and (2) how, in the given situation, can it be used effectively?[9]

While this statement confirms that television can promote efficient learning, it leaves open the question of how to accomplish this goal.

Chu and Schramm organized their discussion under a series of 60 major observations.[10] The observations encompass a wide range of issues relating both to factors which affect learning via television and to factors which affect the use of instructional television within an educational system. Some of these observations are reasonably well established by documented experience while others are speculative, based on limited experience and opinion— and clearly identified as such. An example of the latter is their observation 32: "The lack of opportunity for students to raise questions and participate in free discussion would seem to reduce the effectiveness of learning from instructional television, particularly if the students are fairly advanced or the material is relatively complicated." Most educators probably would agree with this observation. However, in a study published in 1969, Dubin and Hedley analyzed 42 comparative studies of college television teaching and found that regular television was as effective as face-to-face instruction while television with a voice link back to the television lecturer was definitely less effective.[11] This surprising result is, unfortunately, characteristic of the lack of firm ground in the field. It is of interest to note that 39 of the 42 studies analyzed by Dubin and Hedley were completed prior to 1963. Since several instructional television systems incorporating voice feedback have been built in the last few years, and more are planned, further research, studying some of the newer systems, would seem to be indicated.

Although a number of the factors which affect learning via television have been identified, and there is solid understanding about some of these factors, there is only a limited store of organized knowledge which has general relevance and applicability. Chu and Schramm recognize this when they remark:

We are far from having a scientific rhetoric of instructional television, and a great deal of rethinking, research, and reinterpretation will be needed before we have one.[12]

Allen identifies this condition as existing with respect to all audiovisual media:

Although almost fifty years of media research has accumulated, we know with certainty little more than that audiovisual techniques can contribute to learning. Where and how they can contribute the greatest is still under investigation.[13]

But Allen then goes on to further identify this condition as characteristic of our general state of knowledge about learning:

This lack of knowledge, of course, is not unique to audiovisual instruction, but holds for all instruction as well. The crucial point, however, is just what we do know and how this knowledge may be applied to the development and use of instructional media.[13]

Thus, what is known about learning via television is similar in character to what is known about learning employing other media and methods: namely, a great deal in the form of detailed experience and substantially less about generalizing that experience for further applications. There is one generalization which appears to have validity, both on the basis of experience with television and other research on classroom learning: television will not be effective in carrying the entire weight of teaching. One implication of this is that television will be efficient in promoting some kinds of learning and poor for others, that it often will be most effective when it is used in conjunction with other media. Another implication is that a great deal of attention must be given to what happens at the receiving end, in the classroom, to what the learner does in interaction with the televised material. These two implications identify the major learning issues involved in any contemplated use of instructional television.

It is obvious that these issues have been resolved successfully in many instances because there are numerous examples where television has done a good job in promoting learning, and some examples where it has been outstanding. How were these learning successes achieved, where does the experience of these successes reside, and how can it be made available for new applications?

Three general statements can be made about how these successes were achieved. First, in most instances the successful television programs have been developed by teams in which there was genuine collaboration between competent educators and equally competent television production personnel. Second, there has been effective communication and interaction between the production team and the teachers using the programs in the classrooms. Third, the whole development process has been experimental, with both the teachers and the production team alert to what was going on in the classroom and filtering out that which works from that which does not.

A significant part of the experience of these successes resides in the programs themselves, provided they have been recorded. These recorded programs can be studied by educators and television production personnel in the same manner that textbooks can be studied by potential authors and publishers looking for new ways to organize or present material. Another part of the experience resides in reports and papers which describe the way programs have been developed and used in the learning situation and also cite the learning outcomes. Finally, part of the experience resides in the individuals who engaged in the process, the production team and the classroom teachers.

From the standpoint of new applications, the experience which resides in the production team is the most critical. It holds this critical position because it is this experience which incorporates and integrates the dynamics of the production process and is, therefore, transferable rather directly to new applications. This condition carries with it two substantial implications for the development of effective learning via television. First, progress will be dependent largely upon the building up of truly collaborative production teams which integrate the best that is known about subject matter, learning, and television production. Second, past experience says that generating such teams is a difficult and time-consuming process and, therefore, the growth of first class instructional television will likely not be rapid.

Summing up, learning via television is yet in a primarily experimental stage, from a human as well as an intellectual standpoint, with an absence of theories capable of organizing much of the experience for use in new applications. This situation suggests caution in expectations about the outcome of any single application and about the length of time which will elapse before there may be widespread capability to use television to promote learning. At the same time, the situation also suggests that within this framework of expectations there should be continuing efforts to learn more about how to use television through applications to a wide variety of situations in educational systems—but, applications which incorporate evaluation procedures which can add something solid to the store of experimental knowledge about learning via television.

As observed earlier in chapter two, experiments and demonstrations often have had multiple purposes, and therefore often conflicting operational objectives, with the result that when a demonstration ended it was virtually impossible to sort out what had been achieved. Thus, an obvious first priority is to aim for a single educational purpose stated in terms which define how television is going to be employed operationally. Frequently, for political or administrative reasons, the educational purpose is stated in very general terms and will have to be reduced to operational specificity before planning can begin. The degree of specificity will vary but certainly the area (or areas) of learning will have to be delineated since people don't just learn, they learn *something*. Also, there will have to be as much definition as possible (at the outset) of the relationship of the television instruction to other elements in the instructional system. For example, how much of the instruction will television be expected to carry, in what ways will other media be used, what will be the conditions under which television will be used in the classroom, etc.? From the foregoing discussion it is clear that for many of these factors the knowledge needed to make confident planning decisions is lacking—indeed, gaining more knowledge about one of these factors may be the educational purpose. Rather than being a license for sloppy planning, this condition puts an even higher premium on initial planning which is clear about goals and clear about what is or is not known about the methods proposed to achieve those goals.

Out of the past two decades of educational experiment, there has emerged the recognition that the creation of effective learning materials for wide distribution requires a research and development process which involves reiterative testing and revision of the materials until students learn well when using the materials in actual school environments. Out of this experience has come the realization that subject matter knowledge, however profound, is not sufficient to produce effective materials; other skills are required. Learning psychologists have contributed through their work on learning objectives and hierarchies of learning; educational testing specialists have worked with the teachers in evaluating the use of material in the classroom and in analyzing what the results imply for revision; and specialists in the use of print, graphics, film, and television have devised more effective ways of presenting the material. Not only must there be close collaboration with a limited number of classroom teachers during the testing and revision cycles; teachers are also the key to deployment and diffusion of the materials. Teacher training programs must be included in the development planning from the outset.

The implications for instructional television are clear. The subject matter specialists and the television teachers will need to learn a lot about television production, and the television producers a lot about education. People who are capable of crossing lines over to other fields usually are in short supply, and hence it will not be easy to find people in education and in television who can contribute effectively to the production process. This problem will be aggravated in developing countries where there are few people with any television production experience; training of television production personnel will have to be a basic element of instructional television development in such situations. The collaborative nature of the production process is certain to raise organizational issues as to who is in charge. For example, in countries with fairly centralized government control there will be questions as to which ministry controls what parts of program purpose, production, and distribution. These questions will involve not only ministries of education and broadcasting but also other ministries engaged in education, such as agriculture, health, family planning, and labor.

The two extremes of organization and scale for the production of instructional television programs are represented, at one end, by the Children's Television Workshop and, at the other, by a single teacher generating his own programs without the assistance of anyone familiar with television production. Both can produce effective programs for specific purposes, but experience has demonstrated that the single teacher will never produce programs which can fill the role that the "Sesame Street" programs play and, conversely, using the CTW organization to produce a ten-minute supplementary program on the breeding of fruit flies is like using a cannon to kill a mouse.

The single teacher who produces his own supplemental programs for his own courses utilizes television in a way good teachers have always used whatever teaching methods were available and appropriate. This use likely will increase with the availability of videocassette recorders and portable, low-cost video cameras. However, the program's effectiveness usually depends on the way the teacher had conceived and produced it to relate to the rest of his particular course, and out of this context such programs are not likely to be very useful to other teachers.

In producing "The Electric Company," the CTW is engaged in developing something analogous to a textbook, a series of programs which numerous teachers in different schools can use to carry a substantial part of the teaching load in a particular course. Here, where television plays a substantial role in the teaching-learning process, instructional television has the potential to make a major impact on education. Regardless of size, all productions must incorporate the basic elements of team approach and interaction with, and feedback from, the school environment.

The size of the production facilities obviously will have to be geared to the programming effort. A large facility will have capabilities for shooting in either film or television, while a small facility most likely will operate only with television. Developments in television technology will soon give videotape recording a mobility and editing flexibility equivalent to that possessed by film production. A consequence of this will be that the modest production facility will have much the same kind of basic production capability as the large facility although not, of course, the same overall production capability, because of differences in auxiliary studio production resources. For shooting outside the studio on location, however, these technical developments will place the production teams from the large and the modest facilities on much the same footing insofar as overall production capability is concerned. This new freedom might be particularly useful in developing countries where one of the central problems of education is to provide some practical educational alternatives to the classical pattern left by the colonial power, alternatives which have some tangible connection with the existing needs and opportunities within the countryside. With this easy capability to bring the countryside and its problems into the classroom, it is at least possible that some innovative teams will succeed in producing educational programs which make a difference.

One of the decisions facing the potential user of instructional television is the question of whether to use "live" or "taped" programs. Before the advent of portable videotape machines, a live instructional television program was one which was, in fact, being produced at the same time as it was viewed. However, now the term has come to mean programs which are intended to be used only once and then discarded even though, for scheduling or other reasons, they may be taped for showing at a more convenient time. Taped programs are referred to as those which are taped with the intention that they will be used for subsequent presentations of the same course. Some school systems have relied almost exclusively on live programs. Given what is known about the testing and feedback process needed to develop effective teaching materials, a reliance principally on live programs would appear to have two implications: if testing and feedback are not employed, the quality of the programs will likely not be high unless the teachers are unusually qualified and also skilled in the use of television; or, if testing and feedback are employed, the production costs per hour of live instruction will be high.

Yet dogmatism on the question of live versus taped television programs does not illuminate the issue. An instructional television educational package developed with large investment of money and highly skilled human effort obviously will be used for several years in the same manner that textbooks are used; when it is replaced, its successor is likely to have required a comparable investment in money and talent. At the other end of the spectrum, the use of television within a school to make the particular expertise of one teacher available to a number of classes is a sensible use of live television. As always, the means should suit the purpose but, given the state of our knowledge about learning via television, it would seem sensible to be biased towards taped programs. More specifically, within a given budget of human and financial resources, a school or school system will learn more about how to use television effectively if it invests some of these resources in the testing, evaluation, and revision process. This implies giving up at least some live programs—but not live activities for the teachers, since they will be at the center of this improvement process.

An instructional television development process which incorporates classroom pretesting will increase the likelihood of programs that are successful in a school system. The requirements do not differ in principle from those for any effective instructional program: a well defined purpose or set of objectives; instructional materials, of appropriate kind and quality, which make available the informational, conceptual, and demonstrational matter students will require to achieve the learning objectives; suitable stimuli and opportunities for active learning by the students, for them to do something in interaction with the materials, the teacher, or the other students; a well defined—not the same as minutely specified—role for the teacher; and a training program which helps the teacher to understand the educational nature of that role and to get some practice in playing it. Finally, the logistics must be organized to conform to the operational realities of the classroom and the school system.

The central classroom questions are those which revolve around the teacher's role in what goes on in the classroom employing instructional television. Proponents of the widespread use of television in education often have accused teachers of an unwillingness to try television, and in an earlier chapter this resistance has been discussed. One wonders whether there is not at least some analogy between this situation and that of the farmers in India who, a decade ago, were being accused of being irreconcilably traditional and opposed to change because they would not adopt the new agricultural practices and the new rice and wheat seeds being pushed upon them at that time. Subsequent events leading to the so-called "green revolution" have demonstrated that these farmers would change when the potential gains made it worth the risks—and there is general agreement that they were sensible in not taking a risk with the seeds offered them a decade ago. Perhaps the resistance of teachers to instructional television also has included, in some instances, a comparable component of common sense concerning the learning effectiveness and the classroom effectiveness of the instructional television offered them.

Even with a teacher training program, there will be practical problems in the classroom which will complicate matters, at the best, or cause major teacher hostility, at the worst. One of these, which has received little attention so far, is the problem of previewing television material. Unlike a book through which a teacher can scan quickly to get the gist and style, the linear nature of a television (or film) program requires some substantial fraction of the viewing time to sample the program. The visual nature of a television program supplies its particular character, and a written description is not useful unless the teacher has some previous experience with the producer, or the program is part of a series with which the teacher is familiar. The previewing problem would be exacerbated in a school situation in which television programs stored in videocassettes were to play a large part in individualized instruction under the management of the teacher; how would the teacher find time to ascertain the contents of the cassettes?

Another very practical problem for the teacher and the schools is the storage of television programs; considerations of educational effectiveness, space and cost must be resolved. The question of effectiveness has mainly to do with the availability of programs, with respect to both variety and the time required to obtain a given program. Obviously, this question is interwoven with the space and cost considerations, as in any library problem. Of the total cost for a copy of a purchased television program, only a fraction will be represented by the actual reproduction cost of the copy, and this factor may make attractive a central library storage in a system, with cable transmission delivery of programs on demand. On the other hand, a school system following the current trend to provide individualized instruction, with instructional television as a major ingredient, probably would need at least substantial storage in each school to give students adequate access. The Sony videocassette, which can hold enough tape for up to 60 minutes of program time, is only slightly smaller in volume than the usual book of three to four hundred pages. If a six-grade school were to teach six hours per day for thirty-six weeks per year, and to use fifteen-minute units of instructional television per hour in each grade, the school would have to store the equivalent of about sixteen hundred books (if all this television were contained in Sony cassettes, four units to a cassette). Clearly, if television comes to play a major role in education, storage will not be a trivial matter.

The newer aspects of television technology will have their effect mainly in respect to the logistics of reaching the student with the television program. A limitation of open broadcasting is that only one program can be broadcast at a time, and this forces scheduling rigidities on schools. This limitation has been removed by the use of reel-to-reel portable videotape recorder-players which record off the air for later use at a time convenient to the school's own schedule. Videotape cassette recorder-players will make this process easier and undoubtedly will find extensive use for this purpose.

It is not yet clear what will be the role in education of those playback systems which do not have "off the air" recording capability: EVR, SelectaVision, Video Disc, Super 8 film, and perhaps others yet to come. Will the economics work out so that some of these systems find wide use in some school systems? If so, will there be players in each classroom, or will there be a system "library" with several players coupled to a dedicated cable transmission system which delivers programs to television receivers in classrooms within the system? Or, alternatively, will the delivery be to a videotape cassette recorder-player which will record for later use in a classroom? Many possible combinations of use can be thought of, but what will be the costs and actual performance of these systems in the hands of consumers? Until some data on their actual costs and performance become available, the possible future of these playback systems in instructional television will remain in the realm of conjecture.

Cable transmission of instructional television to schools began in Hagerstown in 1956. In the intervening years this use has increased, and undoubtedly will continue to grow in the future. The channel capacity of cable has excited much speculation about other educational and learning uses. As yet there have been few concrete suggestions for program content and little discussion of how to mobilize the tremendous investment—in psychological momentum, human skills, and money—which would be required for program development to exploit this channel capacity for educational purposes. The only major demonstrational use of cable currently funded is the TICCIT experiment described earlier in this chapter. Thus, the future of cable in instructional television also remains mainly in the realm of conjecture.

From the viewpoint of the classroom, satellite transmission of instructional television is entirely equivalent to open broadcasting. For an educational ministry in a developing country, however, satellite transmission may offer an option for the introduction of instructional television on a wide scale a decade ahead of when it might be possible with a ground-based broadcasting system. Thus, from the viewpoint of an educational system, satellite transmission can be significantly different from open broadcasting. The difference will be primarily one of increase in scale—scale of the area that can be served and scale of the organizational, financial, and human resource requirements. Unfortunately, there also will be an increase in the scale of the mistake that can be made if any elements in the chain—program development, teacher training, integration within the school system, or logistics—are poorly done. On the other hand, there will be an inverse scale effect on the time available to develop programming capability: the required capital investment for the hardware naturally will generate pressures for developing instructional programs concurrently in several subjects and early commencement of transmission to a large number of schools. These activities, in turn, will call for a large pool of production and training talent of a kind which is in very short, if not almost non-existent, supply, and for a testing and revision process which probably has never been employed locally. It is in the nature of decisions such as that to employ satellite television in a developing country that the reasons for making the decision will transcend the facts related only to education; the danger is that the decision will ignore these facts and plans will be based on a time scale which is incapable of being met by the human ability and experience available. The use of satellites for education in developing countries is a very real problem in technology transfer, but the heart of this problem lies on the ground and has to do with the transfer of the process of program development. The equipment required to do the job can be supplied on a turnkey basis; the people can't.

The same considerations hold with respect to television transmissions to out-of-school youth or adults, whether by open broadcast or satellite. Whatever the objectives of such transmission—whether in the case of Britain's BBC broadcasting of mathematics programs to Open University students or in India's satellite broadcasting of national integration programs to villagers—the key factors are the content of the programs and what sort of learner activity goes on during and after the broadcasts.

When one steps into the world of costs of instructional technology, and of instructional television in particular, there is some element of stepping through the looking glass. It is a world in which there is a good deal of easy talk about "cost-effectiveness," with the implication that this is a precise indicator, and a good deal of difficulty in determining either cost or educational effectiveness with any great precision. The lack of precision stems from the fact that the whole field of instructional technology is in a relatively early stage of development, and the work thus far has varied greatly in form and focus. Not surprisingly, therefore, this work has yielded little firm and comparable information on either the educational or the operations side. The tendency to imply precision stems from the enthusiasm of advocates to make a good case for their projects and their results; this enthusiasm is related to the tendency of funding agencies, for their own internal or external political reasons, sometimes to press for prior justification for experimental projects whose outcome can be determined only after-the-fact. The basic elements of this world are likely not to alter greatly until some solid knowledge accumulates on both sides of the equation.

The initial hardware costs for a given instructional television system can be estimated with a reasonable degree of precision because the required components of equipment are available on the market and there is extensive experience in assembling these components into systems. Somewhat less precision is possible on estimates of hardware operation, maintenance, and replacement costs because these will depend upon the skill and dedication of the operating and managerial staff, as well as on local work practices. With the step to program production costs, the estimating precision drops another level because productivity in this process is so dependent upon skills and intangible personal factors whose existence cannot be guaranteed at the outset. The lack of firmness in these cost estimates should be kept in mind during the original financial planning for a project, both with regard to the level of original financing and with regard to contingency financing to meet shortcomings which might develop.

The real difficulty comes for those who have to judge whether the estimated costs justify the potential benefits. Thus far there is no evidence that instructional television will reduce costs in an existing educational system. Since teacher salaries represent the major element in school costs, television's most obvious potential for saving money rests in its capability, over time, to bring about a restructuring of the teacher's role. What form such a restructuring might take is yet a matter of conjecture because of limited experience with instructional television which plays a large part in the teaching-learning process. Other benefits, such as greater learning effectiveness, must also be considered. At this time, major instructional television projects should be considered as experimental and not have to carry the burden of cost reduction.

Film

Film Technology

In the standard projection of motion picture film the light is interrupted at a steady rate by a rotating shutter, and during every second or third interruption the film is advanced one frame by a mechanism which engages the sprocket holes in the film. Sound is recorded on the edge of the film in either photographic or magnetic form. To avoid fluctuations in the sound pitch, the film must pass over the sound detecting device at a very steady speed. The conflicting requirements of steady motion at the sound detecting station and intermittent stop-and-go motion at the projection gate are achieved by leaving excess film on either side of the projection gate (forming a "loop") and by feeding film to this loop, and taking it away, with a system of sprocket wheels which rotate at constant speed.

Three standard film formats have found use in education: 16 mm, 8 mm, and Super 8 mm. 8 mm film is equivalent to one-half of a 16 mm film, and thus has sprocket holes along only one side. The Super 8 format has a larger image area than that on 8 mm film, achieved by smaller and differently positioned sprocket holes along one side. Most educational films have been produced as 16 mm prints, but the Super 8 format is finding increasing educational use because of the lower print costs and acceptable screen image quality. Automatic threading 16 mm sound projectors have been available for some time. There recently have come on the market Super 8 cartridge loading projectors which are fully automatic in their operation after the film cartridge is inserted.

For many years there have been 8 mm endless loop cartridge projectors on the market, both very simple silent projectors and more elaborate sound versions. Since the film is in an endless loop, no rewinding is necessary at the end of a program. On the other hand, most projectors have no provision for reversing and if the film is allowed to run by the beginning point there is no way to reach this point again except by projecting the remainder of the program again.

Recently, Norelco (Philips) introduced a Super 8 projector which combines the features of the filmstrip projector and the motion picture projector. It is a desk top unit with a small rear projection screen designed to be viewed only by one or two persons. The projector uses two cartridges, one the standard Philips audio cartridge and the other a somewhat similar, but larger, film cartridge. The magnetic tape in the audio cartridge carries both the sound and a series of magnetic cues which are used to trigger the film advance mechanism. Thus, it is possible to change frames at a rate appropriate to what is being shown. The object of these complications is to save substantial film footage and thereby reduce print costs. Given the complications of producing a film which runs at varying rates of speed, and of synchronizing the film advance cues with the recorded sound, the most likely applications of this system would appear to be in programs where a large number of prints will be required.

Film and Education

Within the areas where the visual presentation capabilities of film and television overlap, what is known about learning from film is what is known about learning from television. Indeed, the research on both films and television has been used in evaluating what is known about learning via television.[14] Not surprisingly, most of the important questions about the production and use of films in an educational system are the same as those for television. The differences which do exist are mainly related to logistics, such as: the greater convenience of television when delivered via cable to the classroom; the freedom to project film on a large screen; the library of programs available on film and not on television; and the historical organization of the production and marketing of educational films. It is likely that this range of primarily logistical questions will be as important as relative costs in determining how much television replaces film in this area of visual overlap.

However, only film has been able to bring into the classroom certain visual effects, imagery, and experience. Some of these effects and imagery have been achieved because of the greater optical freedom and variety provided by film and film processing. Some have been achieved by the editing flexibility possible with film. And some of the experience has been available because of the rich library of experimental films built up over the past half century. Involvement in these aspects of film has not been widespread in education but interest and activity have grown over the past decade.[15] It is possible that this may become one of the more travelled byways off the road of individualized learning for students trying to learn something about the human condition.

During the past decade there has been experimentation with very short films (a few minutes long) which deal with a single concept. Most of these films have dealt with some aspect of science, and many have been produced as part of major curriculum development projects. The aim has been to make these film loops very accessible so students would come to look on them as learning resources to be consulted, much as one uses books. Typically, the films have been made available in 8 mm endless loop cartridges which the student projects himself on a small screen using the silent Technicolor projector. Perhaps this mode of film use may find equally effective applications in areas other than science.

Audio Tape

Audio Tape Technology

In the last few years audio tape technology has improved markedly in quality and versatility as a result of advances in magnetic tape characteristics and the development of inexpensive recording-playback heads of high performance. The one-quarter inch audio tape cassette pioneered by Philips has brought a new order of convenience to the use of magnetic tape. And the wide market which these advances have opened up has allowed the economies of mass production to be operative in the manufacture of both tape cassettes and recorder-players, with consequent low prices. More recently, widespread interest in and demand for recorded music has stimulated the development of tapes and machines operating with eight recording tracks and with cassettes of new design.

A current line of research deals with the development of technology for recording voice such that it is played back at faster than normal speech speed but in such a manner that it is intelligible and understandable. One impetus for this research is the speculation that uses for this technology might be found in education.

Audio Tape and Education

It is natural that audio tapes have found their most extensive use in those areas of education which are heavily aural in character, such as music and languages. Over the past two decades the availability of magnetic tape recording has revolutionized the teaching of foreign languages. The advent of the cassette and the small portable recorder-player has added a new dimension of access to languages: some college students now learn their French while sitting in their cars during the usual morning and evening traffic jams.

But audio tapes also have proven to be effective in many other areas of education. There has been relatively extensive use in connection with filmstrips or slide sequences, with the audio tape holding a commentary on the visual material and cues for advancing to the next slide; the new Norelco projector described in the preceding film section is a sophisticated example of this application. Audio tapes also are being used to present a complete series of lectures designed to complement a textbook or set of study materials. Another kind of application has been the presentation of a single lecture—or a more informal discussion—by an acknowledged leader in a particular field. There also has been use for specialized tasks such as, for example, guidance to students undertaking use of an unfamiliar piece of laboratory equipment, freeing the student to concentrate on the equipment as he receives information about its operation. Another comparable example, from medical education, would be the use of a spoken commentary from an audio tape while a student examines an X-ray film or a histological slide.[16]

As these few examples illustrate, the particular capabilities and convenience of audio cassette tapes ensure that they will find increasing use in education when attention is given to the contribution that recorded sound can make to a learning situation. The economy and ruggedness of audio tape technology recommend it for careful consideration for applications in developing countries, both in formal and non-formal learning.

Radio

Radio Technology

In amplitude modulation (AM) radio broadcasting the antenna transmits radio waves of a fixed (carrier) frequency. The amplitude of these waves is varied at a rate identical to the frequency of the sound to be transmitted, and in magnitude proportional to the strength of the sound. In frequency modulation (FM) broadcasting, the amplitude of the transmitted carrier waves remains constant; its frequency is varied at a rate identical to the sound frequency, and over a frequency range proportional to the strength of the sound. AM radio can be transmitted over large distances because its waves are long, and long radio waves travel over the horizon by processes of reflection from the earth and from ionized layers in the atmosphere. FM radio waves are much shorter and propagate essentially only in straight lines. Therefore, the range of FM broadcasting is much shorter and equivalent to that of television (the FM frequency spectrum lies within the VHF television spectrum).

The transmitting capacity of an FM station can be augmented, within its assigned frequency band, by the addition of what are called subcarrier channels. These usually are called SCA channels, the SCA standing for Subsidiary Communications Authorization, the FCC regulation under which these channels are licensed.[17] The addition of one or more subcarrier channels to an FM station opens up possibilities for interaction between the transmitting station and receiving stations within its broadcast range. The most obvious use would be to employ one or more channels for broadcast back to the transmitting station, to establish two-way voice communication. Another use would be for the transmission of visual materials simultaneous with the main channel's audio broadcast. Several systems designed to operate over telephone lines could be used for this purpose. Slow-scan television could be employed with various kinds of input. An electrowriter, a device which recreates on paper at a remote station what is written or drawn at the originating station, could also be used. A system currently on the market combines the electrowriter with an overhead projector to permit group viewing on a standard projection screen. Different kinds of facsimile transmission devices might also be used. A subcarrier channel could also be employed to transmit printed material to receiving stations by the use of teleprinters. The simultaneous transmission of a second audio broadcast is still another possibility.

A system employing one or more of these options could be developed since versions of all the equipment are available on the market or can be ordered. Fairly simple receivers would suffice because the receiver would need only the capacity to tune in one specific main channel and its subcarriers.

Radio and Education

Research in the U.S. on the use of radio for learning has been limited and has not established the situations or purposes where radio can be effective.[18] Nor has radio been used in the U.S. in an educational role as much as television has. In western European countries there has been much more use of radio, perhaps because the reasonably uniform curriculum allows the concentration of creative resources requisite to the development of high quality programming. The heterogeneous schooling system of the U.S. may explain the relative lack of radio use. Several current series in the U.S. and abroad demonstrate that radio can be an effective educational medium. All are characterized by careful planning for, and organization of, learner activities to be carried on in interaction with the broadcast programs. Some examples are: the two-way FM radio technical updating program for doctors conducted for the past decade by the Albany Medical College; the daily two-way radio instructional programs for children in the "Outback" of Australia; and the NHK radio correspondence high school program in Japan.

Given this positive experience, and given the evidence that motion contributes to learning only in certain situations, it would seem sensible for developing countries to look hard at what they might do with radio. James Robertson, Director of National Educational Radio, has stated:

It may well be that radio will be brought to its full potential in the less well developed countries, where resources are not so great—where entertainment and merchandising do not play so compelling a role as they do in our comparatively affluent society—where there still is a chance that public leadership will recognize in radio a far more powerful servant than we in America have allowed it to become.[19]

Developing countries may be more able to attain real gains in educational effectiveness through radio than through television. A major experiment with radio would require the same methods and high standards of program development and the same process of integration into the school system as would an experiment with television, but the costs would be substantially less. Although the ultimate promise of television may be greater than that of radio, it will be attained only when much more is known about learning in general and about television learning in particular.

Programmed Instruction

Programmed Instruction Technology

Almost a half century ago, Pressey began to develop self-instructional devices which presented the test material to the student and gave him information as to whether he had selected the correct answer.[20] Through the years, Pressey emphasized the use of his devices as an adjunct to other learning devices and procedures, such as books, laboratory exercises, and films. He conceived self-instructional review and multiple-choice testing material as devices which required active participation of the student and provided immediate knowledge of his accuracy. Pressey's work attracted others to this field, and by 1950 there was a fairly extensive literature and experience with a number of testing-teaching and training machines.

During the 1950s Skinner introduced a significant new element to the field of self-instruction with his ideas on teaching, derived from his experiments on operant conditioning of animals. Skinner emphasized the need to provide the student with continuous and immediate reinforcement to shape his learning. Like Pressey, Skinner also stressed the need for individual control by the learner of his rate of progress, and for his active participation. Unlike Pressey, Skinner proposed that learning could be done wholly by self-instruction programs without the need of other materials. These programs consisted of a linear program of small units of material, each followed by a question to which the student was asked to give a constructed answer, as contrasted to selecting an answer out of a multiple-choice set. After he gave an answer, the student was provided by the program with reinforcement in the form of confirmation or correction. Skinner argued that the human teacher was physically incapable of giving all the necessary reinforcement to a class of students working individually and that this inability necessitated the use of teaching machines. Crowder, among others, challenged Skinner's concepts and developed an alternative called branching programming. In branching programmed instruction the sequence of items depended on the answers given by the student. In response to a correct answer, the program might direct (branch) the student ahead, and in so doing skip several items; conversely, in response to an incorrect answer, the student might be branched to some remedial material. While Skinner believed that student response errors should be eliminated as much as possible, Crowder believed that errors were useful in that they revealed the student's lack of mastery of certain concepts or material.

During the 1950s and early 1960s a number of different mechanical and electro-mechanical teaching machines for presenting programmed instruction material to the student were designed, and several were produced commercially. Book formats for programmed instruction also were developed, usually with the items in a linear program being arranged sequentially from one page to the next, and with the items in a branching program being distributed through the book in a scrambled fashion, with the student's answer determining the next page to which he is directed. Programmed instruction using computers also was explored rather extensively during this period. The outcome of this spurt of activity was that, for most purposes, books proved to be the most practical teaching machines, all factors considered. Except in specialized training situations, most mechanical and electro-mechanical devices did not provide sufficient advantages to justify their cost and the additional complications they introduced into classroom logistics and operations. The unique capabilities of the computer proved to add substantially to the learning process by allowing the use of relatively complex branching programs. For linear programmed instruction, the computer proved to add little except cost.

Programmed Instruction and Education

The period of the 1950s and early 1960s was marked by intense research and development of concepts and techniques and widespread use of programmed instructional materials in classrooms. Factors such as the following were investigated: linear versus branching programs; small versus large step; ordered versus scrambled page sequence; partial versus full prompting; reading versus responding; multiple-choice versus constructed response; overt versus covert response; and, delayed versus immediate feedback. Fierce debate on the best approach to programmed instruction ensued. With the publication of solid research results there came the realization that programmed instruction was neither as effective nor as ineffective as its proponents and critics had claimed. Programmed instruction, like most aids to learning, could be useful provided it was intelligently done and tailored.

Perhaps the most significant result of this intensive work on programmed instruction has been its effect on the design and development process for all instructional material. The concept of programmed instruction has required attention to be focussed on the exact nature of the teaching procedure—the necessity of tailoring instruction to fit a particular instructional environment. Further, the nature of programmed instruction has allowed the gathering of objective data on how students, in fact, do use the instructional material. These data, in turn, have suggested changes for reorganization of the subject material or restructuring of the response sequencing for more effective learning; the changes can then be tested objectively in the classroom. Because different teachers use the same programmed material, the role of the teacher and the type of teacher training required can also be examined objectively.

Over the years there has evolved an applied development process in which the programmed instruction product is tested and revised until it meets certain standards as measured by the performance of students using the program in average classrooms with average teachers. While the process is not foolproof, some publishing houses now believe that if they invest sufficient time, talent, and money they can produce effective programmed instruction. As a result, in the last few years they have increased their investment in development of programmed instruction courses and units. The practice is increasingly for publishers to provide student performance data on the programs in order to convince school administrators and teachers that the programs indeed teach what they purport to teach. While it is possible to judge the content and perhaps identify gross flaws by reading programs, the only way to judge how students will learn from a program is on the basis of data on classroom use.

Programmed instruction, developed in this experimental way by interdisciplinary teams, will find increasing use in U.S. education in the coming years. Developing countries probably also will investigate whether they can use programmed instruction developed in this manner by teams of their own teachers, subject matter specialists, media experts, and educational testing specialists.

Programmed instruction possesses several characteristics which make it attractive in the educational context in which many developing countries find themselves. It can provide instructional material whose effectiveness is not critically dependent on teacher capability; its introduction, however, would have to be accompanied by well-organized teacher training programs. Programmed instruction is a form of learning which can be structured to require a good deal of active participation of the learner; this feature could be an educationally productive infusion into traditional educational systems where the learning of even the highest ranking students can be very passive. The experimental process of successive redesign and field testing affords the opportunity to develop instructional material which will have the form and content needed to achieve in the local scene the stated educational objectives. Finally, since the book format is an effective way to present programs, the technology needed to produce the materials will be available locally.

Computers

Basic Computer Technology

All electronic digital computers are composed of four functionally different elements: (1) an input-output system; (2) a memory unit; (3) an arithmetic-logic unit; and (4) a controller unit.[21] The differences in digital computers result from different characteristics of one or more of these four elements. In some computer configurations the arithmetic-logic unit and the controller unit are packaged together in what is called a central processing unit.

The input-output system is the combination of equipment by means of which data, information, and instructions are fed into the computer and the results of the computer processing are fed out. There are a great variety of input devices, among which are the following: punched card or punched paper tape readers; magnetic tape readers; optical character recognition devices; keyboards; remote data units, such as a temperature sensing device attached to a chemical process control computer; and small computers whose output is the input to a large computer. Output equipment is similarly varied, including: card or paper tape punchers; printers; magnetic tape recorders; automatic data plotters; control devices, such as flow valves in process plants under computer control; and cathode ray tubes. Under the heading "Education-Related Computer Technology," below, there will be further discussion on input-output equipment related to the use of computers in education.

The memory is that unit of the computer in which data, information, and instructions are stored for use in the computer processing. A memory consists of a very large number (up to millions) of segments, each of which has the property of having two stable states (usually magnetic states) and remains in one state until action is taken to change it to the other state. The process of creating either one or the other of these magnetic states in the segment at a specific memory location is referred to as writing; and the process by which a state is detected (converted back to an appropriate electrical signal) is called reading from that memory location. Computers frequently have more than one type memory, differing by the length of time it takes to write and read in the memory—the cost per segment of memory being related inversely to this access time. Every computer has some fast access internal memory; usually this memory is of the magnetic core variety, which is based on the use of tiny rings of magnetic material threaded on all the intersections of a rectangular grid of wires. The commonly used slower access memories, usually referred to as peripheral units, are: magnetic discs, magnetic drums, and magnetic tapes.

The arithmetic-logic unit can perform the four standard arithmetic operations of addition, subtraction, multiplication, and division. These units also are capable of being directed to perform simple logical operations. As an example, the unit could be directed to compare two unequal numbers and to produce an electrical signal indicating which is larger. However, although each of the discrete operations the arithmetic-logic unit performs is no more complex than the foregoing simple example, by proper sequential ordering of a series of such small steps a very complicated logical process can be carried out. In fact, the basis of the digital computer's power is this capability to carry out rapidly a very large sequence of discrete logical steps.

The controller, as its name implies, directs the actions of all the computer elements. The input system contains a unit which, on receiving control signal commands from the controller, converts the incoming data, information, and instructions into appropriate electrical signals and directs these to designated locations in the memory. Subsequently, the control unit examines the instructions in a sequential order and issues the directions necessary for the execution of each instruction. For example, if two numbers are to be multiplied, the controller generates control signals which cause the two numbers to be moved from their locations in memory to the arithmetic-logic unit; other signals instruct the arithmetic-logic unit to go through the series of steps necessary to multiply the two numbers, and yet another set of controller signals directs the arithmetic-logic unit as to what is then to be done with the product and the two multiplicands. When the processing of all instructions is complete, the controller issues signals which cause the information stored in specific locations in the memory to be sent to an output unit, which converts these electrical signals into a form appropriate to the output device being used; for example, into the electrical signals needed to actuate a teletype.

The electronic circuitry used to perform arithmetic, logical, and other operations in digital computers is based upon binary representation of numbers (numbers with the base 2). As almost all U.S. children know, only the digits 0 and 1 are needed to represent any decimal number as a binary number. Thus, the electronic circuitry needed for binary arithmetic operations can consist, essentially, of a series of switching operations by electrical elements which can be switched to one of two possible states—as, for example, a magnetic memory segment or, alternatively, a transistor which can be in either an electrically conducting or non-conducting state. When a decimal number is entered into the computer the input unit converts it into binary form, consisting of an appropriate sequence of the digits 0 and 1, and this number is stored in memory by using a sequence of memory segments, each in an appropriate magnetic state corresponding to 0 and 1. In order to provide for the entry, storage and processing of alphabetic information (that is, words) letters of the alphabet are coded as numbers.

As a very simple example of the use of numerical coding of letters, consider a situation where a computer has been programmed to correct spelling mistakes and a student has entered into the computer a sentence which includes the phrase, ". . . I bel*ei*ve that. . ." Assume the computer is instructed to compare all words in each student sentence with words in a stored vocabulary which includes the verb "believe." When the sequence of seven numbers for the word "bel*ei*ve" is compared with the sequence for "believe" the computer will note that there is not agreement in the fourth and fifth numbers. At this point, if the computer also has been instructed to expect the transpositions of "e" and "i" as a common error in the spelling of "believe," then a message can be sent to the student stating that he has misspelled the word "believe."

The instructions by which the controller manages the processing must be detailed, since each operation is the sum of a series of discrete electronic switching steps. Further, the instructions must be expressed in binary form and must conform to the logic of the electronic design of the machine—must be in the so-called "machine" language appropriated to that machine. It was realized early that these requirements would limit seriously the use of digital computers, and efforts were made in two directions to simplify the instruction-writing (programming) procedure. One direction was aimed at simplifying and reducing the instructions needed in machine language. As an example, computers were designed so that the whole series of discrete steps needed for a certain repetitive operation were combined into an integrated sequence which was brought into action by a single machine instruction. The other direction was a similar effort aimed at developing so-called programming languages. A programming language allows a user to write his program using decimal numbers and natural (everyday) language instruction words. This is made possible by a compiler routine, a set of instructions stored in the computer memory, which the controller uses to translate the incoming program instructions into machine language instructions for the computer. Although programming languages usually do not make as efficient use of memory space, or run as fast, as do programs generated using machine language, these factors are outweighed in most instances by the easy programming facility offered by these languages.

During the past decade, there has been intensive development of programming languages and their associated compilers. In many instances, great economies and simplicities in programming have been achieved by the use of single program instructions which the compiler translates into a number of machine language instructions. Most of these languages have been designed and developed to be most useful when dealing with some particular set of procedures or problems. FORTRAN (*for*mula *tran*slation) is a generally applicable language which is organized to be most useful in applications in science and engineering. COBOL (*co*mmon *b*usiness *o*riented *l*anguage) is a language widely used in business applications. SNO-

BOL is a language very useful for non-numerical logic problems and for text processing. BASIC (*beginners all*-purpose *symbolic instructional code*), a language developed at Dartmouth initially to introduce students to the use of computers, has wide applicability. COURSEWRITER, developed by IBM, and TUTOR, developed by The University of Illinois, are languages for use by a teacher in writing tutorial computer programs. These are only a few of the many programming languages.

The increase in the processing power of computers has been both a result of and a stimulus to the developments in electronic technology from the stage of the vacuum tube through the transistor to the present phase of integrated circuits. One consequence has been an increase in the number of electronic components which can be packed in a given volume. This higher packing density has resulted in a lower cost per component and, because of the shorter distances between components, a reduction in the time required for electric signals to travel from one component to the other. The result of this decrease in both unit cost and response time has been a steady growth in the computer processing capability available for a given amount of money. This, in turn, has had two effects: a significant increase in the capability of the largest computers, and a growing production of small—or "mini"—computers, some of which have a capability considered large a decade ago but cost considerably less than these large predecessors.

Over the next decade the trend of reduced cost per unit of computing capability will continue. It is expected that large scale integrated circuit technology will undoubtedly result in functional design changes, for example, through moving some of the logic circuits from the central processor to input-output devices. Improvements in memories also are expected, both in shorter access time and increased storage capacity, although it is not yet clear which technologies will produce these improvements. Much work is being directed towards improvements in the fourth element of the computer—the input-output system—because improvements in the other three elements are causing the bottlenecks on system performance to be located more often in the exit and entry devices.[22]

Education-Related Computer Technology

During the coming years computer hardware will offer to educators an increasing computer processing capability and flexibility at a decreasing unit processing cost. For the most part these improvements will become available for reasons other than potential uses in education. The major technological problems related to educational use of the computer fall within the following three areas which are interdependent: the interface between the user and the computer, i.e., the input-output system; the communications requirements between the user station and the computer; and the programming languages needed for educational uses.

There are two basic modes of user interaction with a computer: "batch" and "on-line." In the batch mode the user prepares his input in advance, usually in the form of punched cards or punched paper tape, and submits this to a computer facility either directly or through a remote input device connected to the computer facility by telephone line; at some later time, after the computer has processed the input, the results are returned to the user. In the on-line mode the user works at an input-output device which is connected directly to a computer and receives his output as soon as the computer has completed its processing. Early computers were used primarily in the batch mode because they did not have either the capacity or the sophistication to accommodate many users at one time. During the past decade, however, computer systems have been developed which can service a large number of users simultaneously. It is likely that this "time-sharing" will become more highly developed in the years ahead, as a consequence of both technological and economic factors, and thus most future educational uses of computers will employ the on-line mode.

The device, or combination of devices, with which the on-line user interacts with the computer is called a "terminal." Originally, almost every terminal used in education consisted of a teletype machine, this being the standard input-output device for practically all early on-line computer use. Teletype terminals continue to be the most widely used terminals in education, both because of their relatively low cost and because they produce a printed record of the input-output message sequence, a so-called "hardcopy."

The first terminals designed for educational use consisted of an alpha-numeric (letters, numerals, and other symbols) keyboard and a cathode ray tube on which the input and/or output messages were displayed; a "softcopy" terminal because it produced no permanent record. These terminals allowed the presentation of graphic displays of a variety and quality not possible with teletypes; line drawings, graphs, three-dimensional views, etc. Devices were incorporated which permitted the user to identify particular spots on the cathode ray tube face; for example, to point to a "yes" or a "no" displayed on the tube. One such device was the "light pen." The light pen contains a photocell and, when the pen is placed against a point on the outer face of the tube, a low level electron beam which is being continuously swept across the inner face of the tube causes the photocell to generate an electrical signal when the beam passes that point; a computer program compares this signal with the known position of the electron beam at every instant of time, thus informing the computer of the position of the light pen.

During recent years, increasingly sophisticated cathode ray tube terminals have been developed and marketed. The most elaborate of these terminals utilize "storage" tubes which can maintain their image for up to 15 minutes, and do not require that the image be "refreshed" 30 times per second as do ordinary cathode ray tubes. Very complicated graphic routines can be executed on these terminals and, further, these can be executed with relatively little communication capacity between the terminal and the computer because of the lack of need for image refreshing. These more complex terminals have not found widespread use in education, and are not likely to, because of their cost.

With increasing experience in instructional uses of computers, there has come growing recognition that there are many learning situations where on-line use of the computer is most effective when combined with the use of projected photographic images and recorded audio messages. There are several efforts being carried on to develop a computer terminal incorporating these elements. The Computer-based Education Research Laboratory at the University of Illinois has developed such a terminal for its PLATO IV system which is designed to service 4,000 student terminals from a large computer.[23] In this terminal the cathode ray tube is replaced by a transparent glass "plasma" display panel in which there are some 260,000 tiny cells filled with neon gas, each of which can be caused to glow (as an ionized plasma), or to cease to glow, by the sending of appropriate electrical signals to that cell. The display created on the panel is bright enough so that it can be seen easily in a well-lighted room; since each cell is either on or off, it is not possible to create multi-tone shadings as on a cathode ray tube.

A random-access image projector, utilizing images stored on microform cards, is located in the PLATO terminal such that photographic images can be projected on the rear surface of the transparent display panel coincident with the display of computer-generated information related to the image. A random-access audio system also can be incorporated into teaching programs or for students to record messages to their instructor. On the front of the panel there can be mounted a sensing grid which can identify any one of 256 separate areas which a student might touch with his finger to identify, for example, some detail of a projected image in response to a question posed by the computer. The grid employs 16 infrared light sources along two adjacent edges of the panel and matching photocells along the opposing edges; the student's interruption of two perpendicular light beams informs the computer of the location of his finger. The grid performs the same function as a coarse light pen, but with much more simple technology.

The PLATO terminal incorporates more features designed specifically for instructional use than other terminal which has gone into production. Every effort has been made to design for low cost and resonable success has been achieved in this respect so that if the terminal proves to be effective it could become widely used. Further, the nature of the display panel allows large economies in communications costs.

Since teletypes are designed to operate over telephone lines, the transmission costs per teletype terminal are in the range of telephone communication costs. On the other hand, a remote terminal using a cathode ray tube display would have a very high communications cost since it would require a bandwidth equivalent to a television channel. Because the PLATO plasma display panel only requires information to be sent when changes are to be made in the display, the total information requirements are about equivalent to that of a teletype terminal. As a consequence, a single PLATO terminal can interact with the central computer over a telephone line, and a remote cluster of as many as 1,000 terminals can be serviced over a communication link which has the capacity for a single television channel.

The National Science Foundation is supporting a five-year demonstration of the PLATO IV system in which up to 2,000 terminals will be located in elementary schools, community colleges, and university classrooms in different locations in the state of Illinois.[24] The University of Illinois will prepare instructional materials for courses in reading and mathematics at the elementary level. College level materials in biology, chemistry, mathematics, and physics will be developed by the instructors themselves. This demonstration should be of sufficient scope and duration to provide answers to questions of effectiveness and costs of the various PLATO system components. It should also yield valuable information about the management and logistics problems involved when a large computer is used to instruct students at different institutions in several different subjects.

The National Science Foundation also is supporting a five-year instructional demonstration of the TICCIT system which has been developed by the MITRE Corporation.[25] The TICCIT system shares with the PLATO system a reduced requirement for communication with remote terminals, but it achieves this reduction by different means, as described earlier in this chapter. This demonstration experiment also will be different in the size of computer, the number of terminals, the kind of terminals, and the number of courses in which instruction is being given.

The TICCIT system will use a mini-computer which will serve 128 terminals over a single television cable. There will be one system installed in each of two junior colleges. The TICCIT terminal will consist of a commercial television receiver, a "frame grabber" such as described earlier, an alphanumerical keyboard, and a sound outlet from audio storage in the computer. In each college there will be instruction in four courses: remedial and first-year English and mathematics. It is expected that about one-quarter of a student's classroom contact hours will be spent in computer-assisted instruction. The courses will be developed with careful attention to performance objectives, learning hierarchies, and other strategies of "instructional design." Thus, the outcome of this demonstration will yield information not only about the TICCIT system but also about what can be accomplished at the college level by a careful and adequately financed application of current concepts of instructional design. The National Science Foundation has arranged for evaluation of the two demonstrations by an independent group.

Effective educational use of computers is dependent upon the existence of a computer language suitable to the particular use. While efficient languages are available for some applications, for some other uses adequate languages do not exist, as, for example, in natural language dialogue between a student and a computer, where the available languages permit dialogue only within a limited context. And there are yet other uses for which a new language may have to be developed, such as the introduction of a new computer system for tutorial instruction.[26] The PLATO group's development

Other obstacles are the result of the rudimentary state of current knowledge about learning processes and how to help students to develop and utilize these processes, and these obstacles are inherent in all instruction. Most traditional instruction goes on within a communications environment in which there is a good deal of message redundancy—in tone, gesture, or glance. Further, in the usual classroom, the amount of feedback from students is limited, and hence there is limited monitoring of the learning experience. When the computer is used, there is little redundancy in the communications, and the feedback is continuous. As a consequence, any lack of knowledge of how students learn will be exposed clearly when a CAI program is initiated, and considerable testing and revision may be required to make a given CAI program effective.

This revision will have to be done mostly on an experimental basis of trying various approaches and finding out what works. Suppes, at Stanford, has been one of the few CAI researchers to study theoretical behavior models which might be useful in analyzing CAI student response data.[34] He commented on the need for continued experimentation:

It might be thought that the developments in cognitive psychology, especially the structuralism of Piaget and others, would provide a basis for going beyond sheer empiricism in considering student responses. Unfortunately, however, it does not take an extended perusal of the literature in cognitive psychology to determine that the models are not sufficiently developed in a mathematical fashion to provide a genuine tool for the analysis of data. Perhaps the best way to put the matter is that the current cognitive theories are simply not specific and definite enough in their formulation of basic assumptions to lead to specific predictions. There simply are not the tools in the writings of Piaget, nor in those of Bruner and others, adequate to provide predictions of differential difficulty over a selection of items drawn from some complex domain like that of elementary arithmetic or elementary foreign-language learning. I do not claim that Piaget or Bruner, for example, have stated that they offer such tools. I merely make explicit the fact that such tools are not available in the theoretical work they have as yet offered us.

I do think, however, that within the general tradition of stimulus-response psychology, tools of an adequate precision and complexity are now available for at least the elementary parts of skill subjects, such as mathematics and foreign-language learning.[35]

Thus, given the general state of knowledge about learning, the development of CAI during the next decade will be primarily empirical. However, the effective CAI programs that have been developed illustrate that empirical research can be both useful and effective. Moreover, the experimental nature of this development in no way diminishes the potential capacity of the computer to be a powerful learning tool.

As with other "things of learning" the unresolved issues of CAI point up the need for greater understanding of the learning process in the classroom. For example, nowhere does contemporary learning theory offer operational suggestions on how the computer should adjust in an interactive dialogue mode with a student.[36] At the same time, the built-in record keeping capability of the computer suggests that in the process of experimental CAI work—such as in the development of interactive dialogue programs—there can evolve research results which will advance general knowledge of learning.

The experimental nature of CAI development also emphasizes the need for careful documentation and evaluation such as NSF's decision to have the PLATO and TICCIT demonstrations evaluated by an independent group. Undoubtedly, efforts of similar thoroughness in a number of subject areas and at varying educational levels will be required before any substantial body of broadly applicable CAI operational procedures will emerge. CAI can work in particular situations—that has been demonstrated. The task now is to develop a knowledge which will obviate the necessity of considering every situation as "particular."

Another educational use envisioned for the computer is as an aid to the teacher in computer managed instruction (CMI). The situation postulated is one where the broad educational goal is individualized instruction and where a decision needs to be made about the next learning steps for a particular student. In the ideal situation there is presumed to be programmed in the computer the operational steps of several practical learning strategies for reaching specific instructional objectives. A set of judgmental routines is also programmed; through these the computer analyses the learning history and patterns of the student and then prescribes the most effective learning strategy and materials to enable him to achieve his next instructional objective. At present this ideal situation can be only crudely approximated in most schools and thus the current value of CMI would appear to be limited. However, as knowledge of learning strategies increases and alternative learning materials become available the role for CMI will be expanded.

Books

Book Technology

Although "instructional technology" immediately conjures up the image of a new, sophisticated device or technique, the book has been and, for the next few decades, probably will continue to be the most widely used "thing of learning." While publishers continue to strive for better quality and lower production costs, it is unlikely that the next decade will see any technological innovations that will alter substantially current production methods. No recent development has revolutionized education as did the post-World War II introduction of paperbacks. It is possible, however, that the increasing practice in U.S. education to deal with "units" of instruction will result in a substantial increase in the publication of small books— almost booklets— which cover only a single unit.

Books and Education

While books are ubiquitous in the educational scene they remain relatively unexploited as an educational device, in the same way that television and programmed instruction are unexploited. There has been relatively little basic experimenting with the book as a learning device;[37] most of the work has been concerned with how best to organize the subject matter in a particular field for presentation in a textbook, but without altering the book or its pattern of use in basic ways suggested by ideas from learning research.

Only within the past two decades have there been serious efforts to evolve a process of textbook development, a process which would attempt to incorporate in the development of textbooks some of the findings from applied learning research. From these efforts has come the realization that textbooks must be developed in a reiterative process of testing and revision, like programmed instruction and instructional television. And, as in the case of these two other technologies, it has been found that the development of effective textbooks requires a team effort.

Since, for the next few decades at least, the book will continue to be the most widely used instructional technology device, it makes sense to assume that it will be possible to make major improvements in the book as a learning tool and to invest extensively in the search for improvements. Certainly, newly gained insights into learning processes will have implications for books as well as for television and computers.

Notes

1. U.S. television uses 525 horizontal lines; there is no world standard on the number of lines, which creates problems of incompatibility of equipment and of videotape recorded programs.

2. "Basic Statistics on Instructional Television and Other Technologies—Public Schools, Spring 1970," in Bulletin No. 7, Advance Statistics for Management, National Center for Educational Statistics, U.S. Office of Education.

3. Stanley Gerendasy, "Cable TV: Revolution in Limbo," *Seminar*, No. 23, March 1972, pp. 18-22.

4. The term "mega" is used to indicate one million and "hertz" to indicate a unit of frequency of one cycle per second; hence, "megahertz" is a frequency of one million cycles per second.

5. Godwin C. Chu, and Wilbur Schramm, *Learning from Television: What the Research Says*, Washington, D.C.: National Association of Educational Broadcasters, 1968.

J. Christopher Reid and Donald W. MacLennan, *Research in Instructional Television and Film*, U.S. Office of Education, Government Printing Office, 1967.

6. Chu and Schramm, op. cit., pp. 3-5.

Stolurow, Lawrence M., "Implications of Current Research and Future Trends," in John P. DeCecco (Ed.), *Educational Technology: Readings in Programmed Instruction*, New York, Holt, Rinehart and Winston, Inc., 1964, pp. 437-438.

7. Chu and Schramm, op. cit.

8. Wilbur Schramm, Philip H. Coombs, Frederick Kahnert, and Jack Lyle, *The New Media: Memo to Educational Planners*, International Institute for Educational Planning, UNESCO, 1967. This also includes a review of the costs in several systems in different countries.

9. Chu and Schramm, op. cit., p. 98.

10. These observations also are included in Sidney G. Tickton (Ed.) *To Improve Learning, Vol. I*, New York and London; R. R. Bowker Company, 1971, pp. 179-182.

11. Robert Dubin, and R. Alan Hedley, *The Medium May Be Related to the Message: College Instruction by TV*, Eugene, Oregon; University of Oregon Press, 1969.

12. Chu and Schramm, op. cit., p. 60.

13. William H. Allen, "Audiovisual Instruction: The State of The Art," in *The Schools and the Challenge of Innovation*, New York, Committee for Economic Development, Supplementary Paper Number 28, 1969, p. 219.

14. Mark A. May and Arthur A. Lumsdaine, *Learning from Films*, New Haven, Yale University Press, 1958.

Reid and MacLennan, op. cit., p. 10.

15. Richard A. Lacey, *Seeing with Feeling: Film in the Classroom*, Philadelphia, W. B. Saunders Company, 1972.

16. C. E. Engel, "Preparation of Audio Tapes for Self-Instruction," *Medical and Biological Illustration*, 21, 1971, pp. 14-18.

17. Kenneth A. Polcyn, "Broadcast Satellites and Other Educational Technology: Possible Key Policy Decision Points 1971-76, Vol. II," New York, Academy for Educational Development, Inc., November 1971, pp. 2:63-2:64.

18. Leslie J. Briggs, Peggie L. Campeau, Robert M. Gagne and Mark A. May, *Instructional Media: A Procedure for the Design of Multi-Media Instruction, Critical*

Review of Research, and Suggestions for Future Research, Pittsburgh, American Institutes for Research, Monograph No. 2, 1966, pp. 132-134.

19. James Robertson, Speech before National Association of Educational Broadcasters, September, 1971, p. 9.

20. The following books and papers provide a good entry into the field of programmed instruction:

John P. DeCecco, (Ed.) *Educational Technology: Readings in Programmed Instruction,* New York; Holt, Rinehart and Winston, Inc. 1964.

Glaser, Robert, "The Design and Programming of Instruction," in *The Schools and The Challenge of Innovation,* New York, Committee for Economic Development, Supplementary Paper November 28, 1969, pp. 156-215.

Susan Meyer Markle, "Programming and Programmed Instruction," in Sidney G. Tickton (Ed.), *To Improve Learning, Vol. I,* New York and London, R. R. Bowker Company, 1971, pp. 293-297.

Karl U. Smith and Margaret Foltz Smith, *Cybernetic Principles of Learning and Educational Design,* New York, Holt, Rinehart and Winston, Inc., 1966, pp. 245-328.

21. Seymour M. Weinstein and Armand Keim, *Fundamentals of Digital Computers,* New York: Holt, Rinehart and Winston, Inc., 1965.

22. Polcyn, op. cit., pp. 2:76-2:90.

23. D. Alpert and D. L. Bitzer, "Advances in Computer-based Education," *Science,* Vol. 167, 20 March 1970, pp. 1582-1590.

24. Andrew R. Molnar, "Computer Innovations in Education," National Science Foundation, Washington, D.C., 1971, pp. 77-79.

25. *Ibid.*

26. Karl L. Zinn, "Requirements for Programming Languages in Computer-Based Instructional Systems," Technical Report for Conference on the Use of Computers in Higher Education, Centre for Educational Research and Innovation, OECD, Paris, March 1970.

27. Molnar, op. cit.

Saury, Claude, and Michel Schell, "Education and the Computer," No. 8 of Innovations Studies (Series C) prepared for the International Commission on the Development of Education, UNESCO, 1971.

28. Dean Brown and Mohammed A. El-Ghannam, "Computers for Teaching," Stanford Research Institute, Menlo Park, California: A series of talks presented at the Second Specialized Course on New Technologies in Education at the Regional Center of Planning and Administration of Education for the Arab Countries, Beirut, Lebanon, 25-30 October, 1971.

29. The following give an overview of the CAI work at the college level:

"Proceedings of a Conference on Computers in the Undergraduate Curricula," Sponsored by the University of Iowa, Iowa City, June, 1970.

"Proceedings of a Conference on Computers in the Undergraduate Curricula," Sponsored by Dartmouth College, New Hampshire, June 1971.

Roger E. Levien, *et al, The Emerging Technology: Instructional Uses of the Computer in Higher Education,* New York, McGraw-Hill Book Company, 1972.

30. Molnar, op. cit., pp. 68-71.

31. Elisabeth R. Lyman, "A Summary of PLATO Curriculum and Research Materials," CERL Report X-23, Computer-based Education Research Laboratory, University of Illinois, Urbana, June 1971.

32. Patrick Suppes, "Computer-Assisted Instruction at Stanford," Technical Report No. 174, Institute for Mathematical Studies in the Social Sciences, Stanford University, May 19, 1971.

Patrick Suppes, and Mona Morningstar, "Four Programs in Computer-Assisted Instruction," in W. H. Holtzman (Ed.), Computer-Assisted Instruction, Testing and Guidance, New York, Harper and Row, 1970, pp. 233-265.

33. Joseph Weizenbaum, "Contextual Understanding by Computers," *Communications of the ACM*, Vol. 10, No. 8, August 1967, pp. 474-480.

34. Patrick Suppes, Lester Hyman and Max Jerman, "Linear Structural Models for Response and Latency Performance in Arithmetic on Computer-Controlled Terminals," in J. P. Hill (Ed.), *Minnesota Symposia on Child Psychology*, Minneapolis, University of Minnesota Press, 1967, pp. 60-200.

Patrick Suppes, "Stimulus-Response Theory of Finite Automata," *Journal of Mathematical Psychology*, Vol. 6, No. 3, October 1969, pp. 327-355.

35. Suppes, op. cit., May 19, 1971, p. 33.

36. Michael Scriven, EDUCOM Conference on Study of Factors That Have Inhibited a More Widespread Use of Computers in the Instructional Process, Skytop, Pennsylvania, November 1971.

37. Smith and Smith, op. cit. p. 329.

CHAPTER FOUR

Some Major Applications
of the Things of Learning

Countries at all stages of development today invoke the various "things of learning" in their educational process. As part of this study, a survey was made of the efforts of the principal donors of instructional technology assistance in less developed countries and of three major applications of instructional television supported by the countries in which they are located—Britain's Open University, the U.S.S.R.'s educational television and Israel's instructional television. Since many of the projects are nascent and others still relatively young, the survey is mainly concerned with roles and plans rather than with results. Just as instructional television has absorbed the lion's share of the research and laid claim to the term (to the extent that, for many, it is synonomous with) "instructional technology", so it has received the most emphasis as a thing of learning in both less developed countries and more advanced ones as well. Television predominates, despite its acknowledged greater cost and, as yet, unproved relative effectiveness.[1]

The five principal donors who have furthered the use of instructional technology in less developed countries are: USAID, World Bank, UNESCO, UNDP, and the UK Overseas Development Ministry. While other private, national, and multinational agencies, including the Ford Foundation, are providing various forms of aid, including aid for education and of an instructional technology type, either the amount for the mass media is small, or the information is vague, meager, or unavailable.

United States Agency for
International Development (USAID)

Educational technology is one of three priority problem areas designated by USAID's Office of Education and Human Resources in the Bureau for Technical Assistance (OEHR/BTA). In a recent discussion of priority problems, the Office explained its interest:

"To explore the potential of educational technology, as broadly defined, to achieve major gains or breakthroughs in quantity, quality, and cost factors in LDC education and human resources development."[2] To the Office, educational technology

includes all the different methods, materials, equipment, and logistical arrangements employed by education to further its work. From this perspective, the entire system and process to induce learning is permeated with applications of technology which are an integral part of the system and which either advance or retard the learning process itself.[3]

USAID aspires to utilize educational technology to promote overall educational reform.[4] According to Joel Bernstein, AID's emphasis is on systems, not on either hardware or software. The purpose is to produce more improved, less costly and quicker learning for more people and to reach them where they are.[5] At the Airlie House Conference, he identified five general principles that AID follows in supporting LDC development:

(a) focussing on pilot projects that may contribute to major breakthroughs in communication;

(b) providing qualified personnel;

(c) developing programs that are problem-oriented, not communications-media oriented, to meet the needs of key problems directly;

(d) developing local competence with stress upon systems-oriented project planning and administration, quality content development, evaluation, and planning for continuing operation; and

(e) considering the cost-effectiveness of multi-purpose communications systems.[6]

Of the total of $160 million that AID has been spending annually on education, about $14 million was spent on educational technology in fiscal year 1971. This represented an increase of approximately $9.5 million over fiscal 1970. For fiscal year 1972 the amount is approximately $10 million. The Bureau's director, John F. Hilliard, says the future amount will not be less than $10 million even though the OEHR total is cut.[7] These figures include both OEHR/BTA's "regular" budget of about $2 million and expenditures out of other AID funds.

Out of the regular budget, the Bureau supports three kinds of activities:

(a) analyses and services ($600,000 to $700,000), such as the projects contracted through the Academy for Educational Development (AED);

(b) empirical research, such as the case studies by Schramm, *et al.*, under the UNESCO-IIEP imprimatur; and

(c) institutional grants of up to $1 million, such as the $1 million grant to Florida State University for the development of its Educational Technology Center. The Center will provide support for the forthcoming Korean project. Usually smaller in amount and shorter in duration, the institutional grants are for training, research, graduate study, travel, and various forms of assistance related to AID objectives.

OEHR/BTA also has access to "special" funds for educational technology projects from two other AID-funding categories:

(a) population, on which AID currently spends some $100 million a year; and

(b) regular "country" programs, which include up to $75 million a year for educational purposes.

OEHR/BTA's educational technology projects compete with other non-technology projects for these educational funds. The larger, long-range projects in educational technology are financed by these special funds; because the allocation is determined by internal competition, it is uncertain. However, since educational technology is one of three priority areas, the amounts available can be projected fairly accurately.[8]

In his plans for the future, Clifford H. Block, the key AID staff educational technologist, has emphasized (in accord with current AID doctrine) both projects that deal with total reform of educational systems and the research that he believes should accompany the process. Three new projects are being financed out of country-wide funds:[9]

1. In Korea, AID will contribute some $10-20 million over five years to add Grades 7, 8 and 9 to the educational system; hopefully, to reduce educational costs below present levels; to make the curriculum more vocational in nature; to replace rote learning with

problem solving; and to expand English teaching. TV and programmed instruction will be the major instructional technologies
used. One medium-sized city will be used as a pilot at the outset.
The World Bank is expected to provide funds for hardware.

2. In Guatemala, AID will contribute $500,000 over two years,
and $2.5 million over five years, in an effort to reach Indian children
and adults who comprise 40 per cent of the Guatamalan population.
A sequential program of useful pre-literacy skills, literacy training,
and, finally, more sophisticated post-literacy skills will be followed.
TV, radio, and audio cassettes will be used.

3. In India, $2.5 million will be spent over five years to conduct
primary education in two areas and junior secondary education in a
third. Simple, inexpensive programmed texts for students and programmed guides for teachers will be used. Two urban areas, Bom-
bay and Poona, and a rural area outside Delhi will be the sites of this
effort. This program is in abeyance pending improvement in the
relations between India and the United States.

Of the educational technology projects previously financed, AID
is most pleased with the TV effort in El Salvador. The effort there is
to restructure the entire educational system, starting at the junior
high school level. Through saturation television, new objectives
have been defined, new curriculum developed, and teachers retrained. There is agreement in AID on two things: (a) a great ac-
complishment has been made, and (b) the reform, refinement, and
improvement must continue. To the latter end, there is built-in
feedback and continuing evaluation by AED-engaged researchers,
including Schramm and his group at Stanford.

AID has prepared, with AED assistance, a handbook on "Educational Technology in Developing Countries" and a 40-minute movie
to accompany it. The handbook is designed to assist countries that
contemplate the use of educational technology, primarily television,
in their educational systems and to serve as a "do-and-don't" check-
list. The movie deals with the Niger and El Salvador projects and
the lessons learned from them.

Many other private and national benefactors contribute to the
cause of instructional technology on a smaller scale. The results of
their labors are reported in two recent publications, one by Clifford
H. Block and the other by Sidney G. Tickton.[10]

In a recent summary, "Key Applications of the Educational Technologies," Clifford H. Block commented on: in-school application
of television in El Salvador, Niger, American Samoa, Ivory Coast,

Colombia, India, Mexico, Singapore, Northern Nigeria, Ghana, and Brazil; in-school use of radio in Kenya and Thailand; computer-assisted teacher-training instruction in Spain; programmed instruction in India; out-of-school literacy, family planning and agricultural applications; "Sesame Street," new "open universities," Japan's high school instruction through NHK, and India's rural radio forum; a Latin America satellite study, India's satellite experiment, rural education in Guatemala, and AID projects planned in Korea and Brazil.

Sidney G. Tickton's paper, "Recent Developments in Instructional Technology in the Developing World," presented at the Educational Technology Workshop sponsored by the Council on Higher Education in the American Republics in May, 1971, is a more detailed discussion of four projects: El Salvador; Niger, a small French- supported project; the American Samoan effort; and the Ivory Coast project in which many donors have participated.

World Bank

In a memorandum of July 23, 1970, Robert McNamara, President of the World Bank, focussed the educational technology interest of the Bank on primary education.[11]

On educational technology specifically, McNamara wrote:

. . .there is a case for well-conceived projects which point the way toward more efficient and economic use of resources for primary education—experimental projects employing instructional television or other modern educational technology, innovations in primary curricula and teacher training, or modern types of school construction. In brief, we should regard as suitable for Bank financing experimental or demonstration projects in primary education which would have a multiplier effect in promoting greater economy, efficiency and the relevance of instruction to the student's own environment.[12]

The World Bank's position on the "things of learning" is outlined in a memorandum of April 30, 1971, "Teaching Materials":

The current trend in education is to supply the schools and the students with comprehensive "packages" of learning materials rather than with disparate sets of books, laboratory equipment, films, etc. Such learning packages may include textbooks for the students, reference books for the libraries, teacher guides, film strips, slides, audio-tapes, maps and working materials, and other equipment for special rooms and laboratories. Those materials would form integral parts of the course and would in most cases be necessary for the full achievement of the learning objectives. A plan for the production of teaching materials should therefore apply the comprehensive package approach to learning, although a proposed project may in the final analysis only include parts of the package—production of laboratory equipment or printing facilities for textbooks, etc.[13]

In September, 1971, the World Bank issued the first in a series of "Sector Working Papers" on its programs and plans. The first paper on education discusses six possible new areas of lending. In addition to non-formal education and training, business and management, and management of education systems, three of the things of learning are discussed: educational radio and television, programmed learning, and teaching materials and equipment. On the use of television and radio, the paper advocated:

Prudently used as an integral part of the education system, these media can be highly effective in the introduction of new curricula, in upgrading of teachers and in the most efficient use of the best teachers for the mass of students. They do not hold out the promise of lower costs per student but because they can be highly effective innovating forces they can, in some cases, provide a much greater educational return from a moderate increase in expenditure.[14]

However, the Report cautioned against what it considered "a serious danger" of educational television, namely that "the hardware installation will precede the program planning and production, organization and teacher training, and equipment maintenance which are essential to the effective utilization of hardware. . . ." The report stresses that "wherever[the Bank] participates in these projects, it will exert a counter influence to the emphasis on hardware."

In its discussion of programmed learning, the Working Paper advocates the consideration of programmed learning for developing countries. It had previously been considered inappropriate in such countries because "in advanced countries [it] has often been associated with a high degree of mechanization and automation." However, the paper buttresses its argument with recent research that indicates the "educational benefits of programmed learning can be delivered through inexpensive books."

Because programmed instruction enables a teacher to work with more pupils, it could have long-term financial advantages for developing countries despite what the Bank terms "a substantial investment at the outset."[15]

In its discussion of teaching materials and equipment, the Working Paper reiterated President McNamara's concern "that one of the great needs in all countries is a better and cheaper supply of locally produced textbooks and simple teaching equipment and materials."[16]

Through June 30, 1970, the World Bank Group financed fifty-seven education loans in forty-two countries at a total of $431 million.[17] Educational project identification and reviews are sometimes carried out as part of the Bank's economic surveys but more often in cooperation with UNESCO missions.[18] Education loans have ranged from $1.5 million to $20 million and have averaged $7.6 million.[19] Educationists in the World Bank do not get a fixed piece of the budget. They are expected to develop projects in accord with the Bank's objectives and to make the case for them in competition with other claims on Bank funds.[20]

In 1970, the Bank was financing television projects in Colombia, Taiwan, and the Ivory Coast. The Colombia project ended because of lack of indigenous interest. Taiwan chose to continue its project without the Bank. Only the Ivory Coast project continues with Bank aid. Two new projects have been supported in the past two years: (a) $200,000 in 1970 in Turkey for television equipment and for an instructional television training center in Ankara and (b) $500,000 in 1971 in Jamaica for studios and consultants for instructional television in the primary and secondary schools.[21]

Two other projects were explored but not supported: (a) instructional television in Niger where, it was concluded, the country's industrial and communications infrastructure is insufficiently developed and (b) a rural radio education program in West Pakistan and what was then East Pakistan, where political unrest and eventual war forced abandonment. Three additional projects may materialize in 1973: (a) an estimated $1.5 million for a transmitter and studio equipment in Venezuela, (b) an undetermined amount for television receivers in Malaysia, and (c) an estimated $450,000 for expansion of the national television system, including some technical assistance, in Iraq.[22]

The Ivory Coast television project is perhaps the best that has been supported by the World Bank (and by UNESCO, France, Germany, Canada, and several UN agencies). It is the most comprehensive and certainly the most publicized project. For these reasons, it may be useful to conclude this section with a quotation that sums up the ideas underlying the project. Pauvert gives the following four-point summary:

1. School education is not the only type of education which is considered as the process whereby a national community can develop a means of expression, a mechanism for social participation available to all citizens.

2. The use of this mass communications medium—television—supported by all other media (radio, newspapers, cinema) should make it possible to bring about a widespread cultural participation, and the school would then become one of the sub-systems of an over-all man/machine system of communication, the operation of which would be linked with that of the political and economic structures—especially with those structures that allow of the conception and implementation of development projects.

3. The use of television in schools, in such a system, is only one of the aspects of the educational process as a whole, since, on the one hand, television provides out-of-school education for young people and adults and, on the other, in-school television is used in conjunction with all the other teaching methods and techniques: programmed instruction and active methods in various forms.

4. The Ivory Coast's televisual education programme can thus be seen as an attempt to bring into being a cultural and educational process extending to the whole of the national community, associated with its development policy, and linking up coherently the various elements of a technology of education, *i.e.*, the different aspects—concerning both organization and content—of the transformation of the entire education system, so that it may better serve the nation and hence at the same time each of its citizens. For this education system, using a communications medium common to all will enable each person to become an active element in his country and its future.[23]

United Nations Educational, Social, and Cultural Organization (UNESCO)

UNESCO work in instructional technology is directly related to its definition of the purpose of educational aid:

(a) in the case of low income countries, helping to supply the teachers, buildings, equipment, materials, scholarships, study abroad, expertise and finance needed to supplement domestic resources for the attainment of reasonable objectives; and in the case of the whole range of developing countries.

(b) helping to relieve bottlenecks restricting educational progress whether quantitative or qualitative; and

(c) improving the cost efficiency, social and economic relevance and effectiveness of education, and aiding its regeneration and renovation.[24]

While UNESCO seeks and supports educational reform, it does not envision the 1970s as a decade of major educational reform. Acknowledging that major reform requires a period of time during which the changes can take hold, UNESCO advocates in the 1970s creation of "the technical and institutional capacity for change" and the initiation of "research and development in education which should show full fruit in the eighties." However, if a propitious situation exists, reform should be supported. In its strategy UNESCO also emphasizes that aid to existing systems must not be sacrificed to the desire for innovation.[25]

The Division of Methods, Materials, and Techniques is UNESCO's principal unit concerned with educational technology. It is directed by Henri Dieuzeide, a prominent theoretician of educational technology and former director of French educational television.[26] The Division is charged with the following responsibilities:

(a) Coordination of the activities of various aid agencies and institutions and the attempt to bring about standardization of equipment.

(b) Studies and promotion of three kinds, which in their entirety constitute a definition of educational technology as Dieuzeide sees it: learning and research on learning; organization and the application of systems analysis to learning, including objectives, content, and method; and delivery systems.

(c) Servicing activities for some fifty different projects in member countries, and a few carried on with UNESCO's "own" funds. Examples are the computer teacher training project in Spain; the Ivory Coast television teaching project; curriculum materials development for television, film and satellite use in India; and a satellite feasibility study in Latin America.

(d) Assistance to member states upon request. Examples are educational system analyses in Indonesia and Brazil.

UNESCO's regular budget, supplemented by UNDP and UNICEF funds, has been used to improve teaching methods, including the use of the mass media.[27] UNESCO spent about $107 million in 1971; $45 million in regular funds, $40 million in UNDP funds, and $22 million in trust funds. Educational technology expenditures were made from each of these categories, the last of which is expected to increase this year.[28] UNESCO has both financed and been active in the Ivory Coast and Niger television projects.[29]

Dieuzeide's division works with three kinds of funds:

(a) "regular" funds of approximately $1 million a year, voted biennially for studies and promotional work by regular staff; two examples are the linking of eleven Asian countries for training in programmed instruction and international cooperation on the educational use of satellites;

(b) UNDP funds for big, long-term projects, and for short-term, ad hoc technical assistance; and

(c) trust funds supplied by member states or by multi-national agencies such as the World Bank or UNICEF and earmarked for specific projects to be administered by UNESCO.[30]

United Nations Development Program (UNDP)[31]

UNDP is one of two grant-making units of the United Nations (the other is UNICEF). The annual operating budget of UNDP is now about $250 million, with voluntary subscriptions from 68 of its 550 member nations. The United States, the largest contributor, donated $87 million in fiscal year 1972. UNDP supports projects in four fields of activity; resource surveys, technical education and training, applied research, and economic development planning. As of August 31, 1971, its approved projects numbered 1,428 with a total dollar cost in excess of $3.3 billion.[32]

The "technical education and training" category, which includes all education projects, entails the largest expenditure with a total of 511 current projects, with a total dollar cost of about $1.5 billion.[33]

In education and training, most recently consideration has been given to three areas: "curriculum revision, work-related education, and use of new teaching techniques, particularly audio-visual means."[34] An advisory panel paper notes that while specific reforms of one kind or another, including experimentation with audio-visual means, have been tried in various countries,[35] the urgent need is for a "fundamental reshaping of the educational and training systems."[36]

The panel advised that educational objectives be defined for each country; moreover, in order for the definition to be accurate, "present and future needs of the society must be analyzed."[37] Although it acknowledges that "radio, television, programmed instruction, etc." could extend the influence of the best teacher, the panel cautions:

But it would be a serious mistake to believe that the utilization of such new technologies is in itself a guarantee of better adapted teaching methods.[38]

Through August 1971, UNDP assisted (or approved for funding) three major projects in instructional technology:

(a) the Ivory Coast educational television project ($1,565,100), with UNESCO as operating agent;

(b) two parts of the India TV satellite program, the TV production and studio technical operations training center at Poona ($1,147,000), through UNESCO, and the experimental satellite earth station at Ahmedabad ($1,068,900), with the International Telecommunications Union as agent; and

(c) a feasibility study for a regional ETV satellite for the Americas ($832,900) through UNESCO.[39]

If the advisory panel recommendations are observed in the future, it is unlikely that "ad hoc" procedure in grant-making in instructional technology will exist. According to the UNDP staff, five-year development plans increasingly are being required of countries seeking aid, and these plans must include the objectives of the program and their role within the country's overall development plans. Presumably this requirement includes specificity about the uses of instructional technology.[40]

U.K. Ministry of Overseas Development

In a 1970 White Paper, the British government articulated its philosophy and purposes of future aid to education in developing countries.[41] The Ministry of Overseas Development stressed that frank discussion between the donor and the recipient must determine policy;[42] that multiple donors should collaborate;[43] and that aid to education must always be seen as part of the total aid to a particular country.[44]

Britain's considerable expertise in the use of media and its ability to contribute in the future were also discussed.[45] To make its contribution, Britain will rely heavily on the newly reorganized Centre for Educational Development Overseas. In CEDO, broadcast (both radio and television), curriculum, and audio-visual activities will be combined. Formerly, audio-visual aids, curriculum development and television were each the province of a separate overseas agency.

ODM goes on to say that CEDO will deal not only with curricula but with educational technology and with the organizational implications of change and will be financed at roughly £500,000 annually.

The new CEDO is charged also with advising ODM on proposals for aid in curriculum and media development. "It is not at present possible to estimate how much of our financial aid will be applied in this way."[46]

For 1970-71 (ended April), CEDO's budget was £406,000, of which £256,000 came from ODM and £150,000 from sales, gifts, and grants. For 1971-72, the expenditure level is £410,000, of which £330,000 comes from ODM and £80,000 from sales, gifts, and grants. ODM will boost its total to about £500,000 annually, but CEDO will be expected to continue to obtain funds from other sources for anything beyond its basic program.[47]

After the costly lessons of the 1960s, CEDO, like several other agencies in Britain and elsewhere, will emphasize software rather than hardware; less expensive, less exotic media; increased use of radio; and multi-media rather than single-medium approaches to the solution of educational problems.[48]

Film production is being phased out, and television production will be de-emphasized because both are too costly. Radio, especially radio-vision, a tape-slide combination, is being advocated because of both its effectiveness and its low cost. Program activities are being tailored to the needs, wishes, and capacities of the client countries. The new program includes more nonformal components in such areas as health and work. CEDO strives to ensure that programs initiated with its technical and financial assistance continue after it withdraws; i.e., that trained personnel remain and the costs are covered indigenously.[49]

Ford Foundation

When the Ford Foundation embarked on a program of national scale in the early 1950s it created two subsidiary funds devoted to education: the Fund for Adult Education and the Fund for the Advancement of Education. Both early embarked upon activities involving television as a means of accomplishing some of their purposes. At the same time, the Foundation began an active association with television that continues, with shifting emphasis, changing purposes, and successive direction, to this day.

The Fund for Adult Education provided much of the initial impetus and support needed to reserve non-commercial television channels for educational purposes. It helped the educational broadcasting fraternity to mobilize support for the allocation of channels; assisted citizens committees that raised money to support the fledgling stations, and otherwise helped them to get on the air. In addition, it created the programming service that became National Educational Television (NET).

In line with its charter, the Fund for the Advancement of Education examined ways in which television could be used for instruction. It sought to restructure teacher education; to reform curriculum; to improve the quality of instruction; and incidentally to increase the supply of teachers and reach more students with the improved education.

From these efforts came an early closed-circuit television teaching experience at New York University; the so-called Hagerstown experiment in which the schools of Washington County, Maryland, were linked by TV; "Continental Classroom" courses over commercial television in physics, taught by Harvey White; and chemistry, taught by John Baxter; a humanities TV course in Boston; a Midwest Program in Airborne Television (MPATI); a Chicago City Junior College TV College; and a National Program in the Use of Television in the Public Schools, in which large-class TV instruction was tried in various American cities.

At this time, the Foundation also explored ways in which commercial television quality could be upgraded. The result was Robert Saudek's TV Workshop whose major effort was *Omnibus*, a high-level, much acclaimed but modestly watched excursion into quality informational, cultural and entertainment programming.

In the 1960s the Foundation instituted a program of support for released time of faculty members to teach televised courses at the college level.

In more recent times, the Foundation's domestic activities in instructional technology have included support for the Children's Television Workshop's "Sesame Street," a pre-school level series, and "The Electric Company," a program aimed at helping children in the early grades learn to read; extensive efforts to stabilize both national and local public broadcasting; assistance to establish patterns of policy and operation for cable television and satellites; and exploration of the use of computers in teaching and learning.

While the Foundation has invested heavily in domestic instructional television, its expenditure internationally has been comparatively modest (some $3.5 million to date). The purposes have included a mobile audio-visual unit for Burma; physics films for

Greece; school broadcasting for students and teachers in Nigeria; ETV in the Delhi school system; an ETV pilot project in the Philippines; ETV facilities for the Monterrey Institute of Technology in Mexico; closed circuit ETV in Sao Paulo; general support for the Asian Broadcasting Union; a language laboratory in Zambia; ETV in Colombia; a computer system at the Indian Institute of Management in Ahmedabad; and general support for Britain's Centre for Educational Television Overseas (now a part of the Centre for Educational Development Overseas—CEDO).

Over the past 20 years, little support has been given to educational radio, mainly for two reasons: TV was newer and seemed to have greater promise and, conversely, radio was older and seemed to have attained its own supportable level of moderate effectiveness.

Britain's Open University

Britain's Open University, established to further the objective of greater educational opportunity at both undergraduate and postgraduate levels, has drawn much attention.[50]

In the Report of the Planning Commmttee, the need, the means of fulfillment, and the concern for quality are articulated:

The whole concept of part-time higher education, of the acquisition of degrees by correspondence courses supplemented by broadcast teaching, was sufficiently revolutionary to have led to considerable scepticism in the academic world and among the lay public. As our investigations and discussions have continued, we have found little basis for such doubts. The evidence as it has accumulated has led us inescapably to the conclusion that the Open University is needed, and can function satisfactorily. To satisfy the need requires that the degrees of the Open University shall stand comparison with those of other universities. We are thus greatly concerned to ensure the quality of the staff and the standing of the graduates.[51]

Since its inception, the British Broadcasting Corporation has been heavily committed to educational broadcasting, both for classroom use and for general viewing and listening. According to BBC's Richmond Postgate (Controller, Educational Broadcasting) its relationship with the Open University is BBC's first experience as equal partner in a joint educational enterprise. The BBC Controller of Educational Broadcasting is a member of the University Council. Courses are prepared by an academic team that includes BBC representatives, fourteen of whom are members of the University

Senate. The team is totally responsible for everything: substance, production, textbooks, and all of the materials and things of learning.[52]

Peter Montagnon (Assistant Head, Further Education, BBC), believes that a particular strength of the radio and television material BBC produces for the University is that "it is done in the open" and hence must be continuously tested and assessed. Not only does BBC have full representation on both the Council and the Senate of the University, but the BBC members "may be better qualified educationally in terms of degrees and academic labels than the University staff. This is clearly not a case in which the 'educators' can look down their noses at the broadcasters."[53]

The BBC has a contractual arrangement with the Open University. The University purchases BBC's services at cost plus 10 per cent. The following paragraph on costs is quoted from the Eurich-Schwenkmeyer report, in which the figures are attributed to the *Sunday Times,* January 3, 1971:

Annual operating costs are estimated at $15.8 million for the first year; $9.3 million in recurring costs (for full-time staff at Walton Hall and the regional headquarters, and a healthy $3.6 million slice for BBC) and $6.5 million in direct student expenses (correspondence texts, part-time tutors, local study centers, summer schools, and examinations). With an enrollment of 25,000, this comes to about $632 per student, far below the $2,000 to $2,400 per student cost at many new British universities.[54]

BBC produces both audio and video tapes for both on-the-air and off-the-air (cassette) use. In effect, these are purchased by the University, which is attempting to sell them through its own marketing division. BBC is producing an inventory of 300 radio and 300 TV programs. Initially, four foundation courses were produced: one each in mathematics and science (to help meet a national need for technologists) and one each in literature and social studies (to respond to the humanities-arts orientation of the consumers). Related courses are being added to each major group, and new units are being produced in technology and education.[55] After four years, the programs, which run for 30 minutes, will be revised or discarded.

Although the Open University was initiated as a projected "University of the Air," it is in reality a home study enterprise. Of the ten hours per week expected of each student for each credit, one hour (half in radio, half in television) is devoted to broadcasting and nine to printed media (books, pamphlets and study guides). Indeed, the

Open University is becoming a vast publishing enterprise and dependent as such, to a large extent, upon a complex distribution system. (During the 1971 mail strike, the whole operation undoubtedly would have ground to a halt if the strike had continued.)

The University almost certainly will also become a center of research in learning theory and curriculum development, thus functioning in accord with the predominant British definition of educational technology. No one in the Institute of Educational Technology, an integral part of the Open University structure, seems primarily interested in machines or gadgetry. Since questions of purpose, process, procedure, and substance predominate, the Institute might be called more accurately an institute of educational research.

USSR Educational Television

USSR educational television operates throughout the Union of Soviet Socialist Republics. Reportedly, there are 100 TV centers in the USSR, including a major center in each of the fifteen republics, each broadcasting in its indigenous language. Some programs are taped in Moscow, and the local language is dubbed at the point of broadcast. For this report on the things of learning, the educational television facilities in Moscow and Leningrad were studied.

USSR-TV Center, Moscow[56]

In Moscow USSR-TV operates four TV channels: one national, three local. Channel 1 is the national outlet for political and general information and news. Channels 2 and 4 are devoted mostly to local cultural, informational, entertainment, and sports programs for the Moscow area. Channel 3, the educational outlet, broadcasts both in-school and out-of-school programs of both a formal and an informal kind. Broadcasts cover an area with a radius of 150-200 kilometers around Moscow. Although on occasion four channels broadcast simultaneously, more often two, sometimes three, are in operation at the same time.

In 1967, USSR-TV completed (and subsequently equipped and occupied) a massive studio, headquarters, and transmitting facility. The complex contains twelve studios of various sizes, the largest 1,000 square meters, and an impressive complement of cameras (color and black-and-white), videotape machines and lighting and control equipment, all manufactured in either Moscow or Leningrad. Channel 3 (the educational station) programs are not yet broadcast from the new center but continue to originate in the older studios.

USSR-TV produces a variety of programs aimed at continuing education. For professional people (doctors, engineers, managers, teachers, economists, agronomists, etc.) it broadcasts programs of varying lengths and frequencies, usually after 6 p.m., called "Screen for (name of profession)." On these programs, the latest developments and new methods in the profession are discussed. Viewing is not wholly voluntary. Doctors are directed by the Moscow health authorities to watch, and subsequently they receive a refresher-course certificate. Teachers learn of new developments in pedagogy and of curriculum changes. Engineers and managers are urged to watch programs directed to them; by doing, they gain recognition and added consideration for promotion.

"The People's University," a 45-minute Sunday program, informs peasants, workers, farmers, and others of national achievements and provides a link to the cultural life of the Soviet Union. Programs designed to increase agricultural production are viewed at "Palaces of Culture" on TV sets purchased by the collective farms. In rural areas, these programs are followed by group discussions. Other programs are directed to urban workers. Broadcasts intended to improve speaking and reading ability are said to attract viewers of all ages.

Programs for grades 2-10 are broadcast daily to schools. Produced in cooperation with teachers, the school programs suit the broadcast to the school's schedule, are usually 25 minutes long and coordinated with the classroom lessons. They are aired between 10:00 a.m. and 1:00 p.m. Evening programs, viewed by the students at home, are of 40 to 45 minutes duration.

After 6:00 p.m., special programs are televised for university and institute students. These are all lectures, mainly for first and second year students, and mainly in hard subjects such as mathematics, chemistry, physics and mechanics. Laboratory work must be done in laboratories at the University or institutes. Some lecture courses are completely by television. Many viewers are registrants in institute correspondence courses who combine TV and correspondence at home with lab work, seminars, and examinations at the institutes.[57]

The two key figures in ETV production are the "editor" and the "director." The editor is an expert in the subject. He may be a teacher, but he may also be a non-teaching expert in the discipline. He selects the lecturer from a university or institute faculty or from among other experts (working scientists, historians, writers, etc.) adept at combining substance and showmanship. The editor controls the production until the program is ready for airing. At this time, the director, a TV expert, becomes responsible for televising the program as effectively as possible.

Because the cost of ETV is paid from the USSR-TV budget, not from the Ministry of Education, the television authorities, not the educators, have the final word. Television *for schools* is an additional cost; no saving occurs, and none is intended. Its purpose is to improve quality, not to resolve or alleviate quantity problems.

Conversely, television for higher education replaces some of the earlier non-TV efforts and facilitates the process of instruction because it eliminates the need for travel from home or place of work to university or institute. Thus, the USSR-TV staff maintains, it results in lower costs. They contend that it improves quality only incidentally, as it incorporates visual elements of instruction not possible in the classroom. However, they conclude that by delivering a better service (to more people), it does in fact have a qualitative advantage.

No systematic audience measurement has been conducted. In schools, viewing is required, and pupils are counted. Estimates of regular audiences are based on viewer requests for application blanks and on registration for educational programs. One offer elicited 8,000 letters.

While the TV people say radio could perhaps be used for educational purposes, they believe that television has a greater impact.

Northwest Correspondence Polytechnic Institute, Leningrad[58]

When television came to Leningrad in 1964, NCPI took the lead in developing the use of TV in instruction. The Institute staff became interested in TV after reading articles on its use in the United States and Japan. According to authorities, NCPI now occupies the key leadership role in TV teaching in the Soviet Union. It is responsible for all ETV in Leningrad, which has three channels: one is used for educational purposes; *i.e.*, broadcasts to the schools, another for higher education institutions (including Leningrad University), and the third for the people generally. Committees of educators and TV station representatives work out the programs and distribute the schedule to all educational institutions both in the city and in the 130-kilometer radius area of coverage and to the newspapers. On two days a week, the Leningrad ETV broadcasts are directed to the lower schools; on the other three, to higher educational institutions.

NCPI also uses closed-circuit television. A simply equipped classroom is used for originating telecasts of lectures; these are transmitted to other classrooms equipped with TV sets. While the lecturer can monitor both his own performance and the students' conduct in other classrooms, two-way communication is not possible. Although NCPI cannot at present transmit to downtown Leningrad studios for rebroadcast, the Institute hopes this will come about within the next two years.

All broadcasts are live because the Institute believes that students benefit more from a live lecturer. Content is not standardized (frozen). There is no taping and thus no re-runs nor tape distribution. In Leningrad, instructional television appears to have five purposes:

    (a) to convey information;

    (b) to handle larger number of students without a corresponding increase in staff;

    (c) to forestall conduct by young people considered improper by their elders;

    (d) to improve quality; and

    (e) to save money.

Leningrad Polytechnic Institute[59]

LPI has recently installed an internal, closed-circuit TV system (one studio, one control room, fourteen TV-monitor-equipped classrooms, including two that seat 250 each) in a new building on the LPI campus. The small lecture room-TV studio is equipped with five cameras in a relatively sophisticated electronic switching system that the teacher can control. One overhead camera is used very much like an overhead projector, transmitting what he writes or draws on the desk top in front of him. Audio (but not video) exchange is possible between the teacher and students in any of the receiving classrooms. (This setup is similar to installations in several U.S. engineering colleges.)

Courses now taught on TV are structure of materials, metallurgy, mathematics, and foreign languages. For LPI, television has two purposes: (a) to enable one lecturer to reach a number of students (the maximum now is 1,000) and (b) to bring the student closer to whatever it is the lecturer wants to see (slides, including microscopic slides; film, both 35 mm and 16 mm; drawings, sketches, equipment, demonstrations, etc.). In the not too distant future, LPI expects to add a color capability, to originate programs in science laboratories, and to extend the system to other buildings on campus.

In addition, LPI professors deliver some of the lectures on the Leningrad educational TV channel. The audience for these is its own students (especially part-time, preparatory, and correspondence students); students at other institutions within the station's reach; or adults who seek higher education. LPI staff members also serve on the committee that coordinates the program of the city's ETV channel.

A Summary View of ETV in the USSR

In its schools, the USSR utilizes as teaching aids as many technical, mechanical and electronic devices as the education budget and the sophistication of the teachers will allow. Systematic, and centralized testing, approval, and distribution of the devices have been developed. Through these devices—which extend but do not replace the teacher's ability—the USSR seeks to improve the quality of the student's educational experience.

In open-circuit telecasting, on a special educational channel, programs augment and supplement the classroom. In Moscow, 300 hours a year are coordinated with the school curriculum and produced with the advice and assistance of teachers. The cost, borne by the USSR-TV budget, is in the neighborhood of $770 an hour. Closed-circuit television is used some but not extensively; and when it is used, the purpose (in the one demonstration school we visited) is usually to monitor student reaction in the use of experimental equipment and, only incidentally, student conduct.

Soviet authorities have considered extending the effectiveness of a single teacher to more students than a classroom can contain, but little has been done in that direction; open-circuit enrichment TV is relied on to do this.

In higher education, primarily (almost exclusively) at the polytechnical institutes, which enroll substantial numbers of part-time students, television is the principal new addition to the array of traditional instructional devices. Open-circuit lectures are combined with outside correspondence work and inside laboratory work and examinations. The purpose is only incidentally qualitative; primarily it is an effort to distribute more education to more people at less cost, by reducing or at least not increasing the number of faculty members, buildings, and other facilities concomitant with increased enrollment. Closed-circuit TV is used to reach multiple classrooms (and hence more students) with the same lectures and/or demonstrations.

All broadcasts are live because pedagogical doctrine says a lecture should not be frozen; at present, no taping and tape storage and distribution capability exists. Nor is there so far a capability for originating telecasts in the institutes and piping them for broadcast via central open-circuit educational channel. At Moscow State University, the highest educational level, there seems to be only peripheral interest in TV, although it is used in geology and journalism. For teachers and members of other professions, regular refresher broadcasts serve as one means of retraining and retooling.

In the Soviet educational system, there is a clarity of purpose quite different from our own more diverse and diffuse multiple aims and objectives. Soviet education and hence the uses of instructional technology are tied closely to the productive capacity of the nation and to the strengthening of the economy. In terms of the educational purposes it was designed to advance, the Moscow and Leningrad educational television projects are extremely effective. However, as in other countries, the level achieved in two major metropolitan centers may not be representative of the quality and effectiveness in other, less developed areas.

Israel Instructional Television[60]

Hanadiv, the philanthropic foundation of the Rothschild family, provided the first support for instructional television in Israel.

It began its initial exploration in 1962. To operate a pilot project, Hanadiv created and financed an autonomous organization known as the Instructional Television Trust. Experimental telecasts began in March 1966. In April 1969 the Trust was replaced by the Instructional Television Centre, and the responsibility was transferred for a two-year experimental period to the Ministry of Education and Culture. In April 1971 the experimental period ended, and ITC became a permanent part of the Ministry. ITC has completed its first year of full operation under the Ministry, and its budget for the fiscal year that began in April 1972 was substantially increased.[61]

Israeli ITV has benefitted from a fortuitous combination of timing, circumstances and influences, present and created during the early period. However, as ITV expands, other variables, possibly deleterious to its effectiveness, are materializing. The reasons for the efficacy of Israeli Instructional Television and those that may impede it in the future have direct and indirect applicability to many other projects, experiments, and demonstrations of instructional technology.

Historical Timing. In Israel, instructional television preceded commercial television. Education, not entertainment, was the objective. Yet, as ITV has evolved in ITC, and as, paradoxically, it has become a part of the Ministry, it has become more entertainment-oriented; less didactic in form; more sprightly in presentation; more appealing to the children; and more capable of sustaining audience interest. However, entertainment TV is now available, continually improves, and demands more time, and teachers and students are no longer enamored of the novelty of ITC. The Minister is determined to have a second (educational) channel, not just for "regular" TV but for the new "open university" he hopes to create.

Leadership. Successive Ministers of Education and Culture have given ITV unfailing moral support, increasing financial support, and continuing political clout. Much of the credit for ITV's present acceptance and support in Israel belongs to the individual who was, until recently, the Director-General. He spent four years as a secondary school teacher; he was a personal aide of the previous Minister preceding the present one; and he works closely with influential people in the Ministry, including the current Minister.

Generous financial support. No money request has ever been turned down, and Fiscal 72-73 was up a third over Fiscal 71-72.

Sufficient planning time. Because of Rothschild funds, Israeli ITV had three years of crucial lead time for experimentation and error, and was not under pressure to demonstrate quick success. A gradual progression from experimental to regular use of TV was the result. Now that ITC is a part of the Ministry of Education and Culture, however, it is subjected to all the constraints that surround a governmentally-controlled and financed agency. All civil service regulations apply. Employees cannot be promoted, rewarded, transferred, or discharged without elaborate routine and ritual. Promotion and salary increases now depend upon educational degrees, scarce among the performing and creative individuals who people television.

A small, comprehensible, coverable universe. Israel is a small country. One station covers the entire territory. The "establishment" is small, elite and known; personal acquaintances are numerous, close and lasting. ITC is a part of the in-group, and its proponents have capitalized on this position.

Modestly stated hopes. Television was always considered only part of an integrated larger whole. It was not held responsible for the entire educational process. Nonetheless, it has accomplished three important "other" purposes:

(a) it has speeded the adoption of new curricula;

(b) it has motivated students to learn; and

(c) it has been a major force in upgrading the capacity of teachers. It has been touted as an aid to, not a replacement of, the classroom teacher, and is adapted to—not in control of—the classroom schedule.

Qualitative, not quantitative, purposes. The purpose has been qualitative—to improve what's there—rather than quantitative—to reach more. ITV's desire to ensure quality led quickly to its involvement in curriculum reform and revision. While this concern has resulted in more effective television, it may precipitate jurisdictional disputes. Refusing to abdicate to television, the curriculum people created the Centre for Curriculum Development. They were followed by the educational technologists who contend that ITV is only part of the whole of multi-media. Now there is also a new Centre for Educational Technology, generously financed ($2 million) by Rothschild for an extended experimental period (four to five years). Since many of their interests and projects overlap, conflict seems inevitable.

Involvement and training. Classroom teachers and curriculum advisers are on the production teams for regular lesson telecasts; their opinions are solicited and heeded. Teachers are continuously trained and retrained to appreciate, understand, and utilize the TV lessons. Special teacher workbooks and manuals are prepared. Three times a year, teachers attend special seminars held at one of ten training centers scattered throughout the country.

A psychology of acceptance. The ITV staff has sought to create a climate of acceptance among teachers and school administrators. Science, mathematics, and foreign languages were the first subjects offered on television because teachers were least capable with them and thus would be less antagonized by television instruction on these subjects. Moreover, the first television sets were paid from ITC's budget, not the school's, thus minimizing school administrator resistance. Yet, teachers continue to debate the effect of ITV on their roles as motivators, attitude creators, and directors of learning. If ITV expands, their latent resistance may become overt, disruptive, and detrimental.

Continuous research feedback. Research serves both planning and revision. A research director and staff conduct and plough back into the programming a research component of considerable sophistication and size in both substance and methods (in both teaching and TV technique).

The ultimate role of television for education in Israel is not yet determined. However, in Israel, as elsewhere, the controversy illustrates that television does not merely transmit knowledge. It drastically affects the substance and tends to change education. Television transforms education and the method of teaching; it restructures the teacher's role and the system in which the teacher functions.

Notes

1. Discussion based primarily on interviews and visits in the various countries.
2. *Priority Problems in Education and Human Resources Development—the 1970's,* November 1970, Office of Education and Human Resources, Bureau for Technical Assistance, USAID, p. 2.
3. *Ibid.,* p. 25.
4. *Priority Problems in Education and Human Resources Development—the 1970's,* November 1970, Office of Education and Human Resources, Bureau for Technical Assistance, USAID, p. 25.
5. Joel Bernstein, verbal statement at Airlie House conference, November 22-23, 1971.
6. Kenneth A. Polcyn, *Broadcast Satellites and Other Educational Technology: Current Status and Associated Issues,* New York: Academy for Educational Development, Inc., November 1971, pp. 6, 40, 41.
7. John Hilliard, Interview November 22, 1971.
8. Clifford H. Block, Interview August 25, 1971.
9. *Ibid.*
10. Clifford H. Block, "Key Applications of the Educational Technologies," Appendix A to *Draft Working Paper on Educational Technology,* (Washington: AID BTA/OEHR, November, 1971); and Sidney G. Tickton, "Recent Developments in Instructional Technology in the Developing World," Appendix I to Communications Technology and the Crisis in Education: A Report on the Bahia Workshop (Washington: Council on Higher Education in The American Republics, 1971).
11. "Lending in Education," Memorandum, July 23, 1970, International Bank for Reconstruction and Development, International Development Association, p. 5.

12. *Ibid.*, p. 8.

13. World Bank, Memorandum, April 30, 1971, Mats Hultin, p. 3.

14. *Education Sector Working Paper*, World Bank, September 1971, p. 20.

15. *Ibid.*, p. 21.

16. *Ibid.*, p. 21, and "Lending in Education," Memorandum, July 23, 1970, *op. cit.*, p. 8.

17. *Education Sector Working Paper*, World Bank, September 1971, p. 14.

18. *Ibid.*, p. 18.

19. *Ibid.*, p. 18.

20. Shigenari Futagami, Interview, September 14, 1971.

21. *Ibid.*

22. *Ibid.*

23. Jean Claude Pauvert, "Educational Television in the Ivory Coast," in *Educational Broadcasting International*, Vol. 5, No. 1, March 1971, pp. 44-45.

24. H. M. Phillips, "Resources for the Second Development Decade," UNESCO, Draft Paper, November 23, 1971, p. 9.

25. *Ibid.*, p. 19.

26. Henri Dieuzeide, Interview December 9, 1971. Some of the most sophisticated writing on the evolving thought surrounding educational technology and on the use of the things of technology has been produced by Dieuzeide, and the reader is referred particularly to two of his articles: "Educational Technology and Development of Education," International Education Year (Paris: UNESCO, 1970), and "Educational Technology: Sophisticated, Adapted, and Rational Technology," International Commission on the Development of Education, (Paris: UNESCO, 1971).

27. H. M. Phillips, op. cit., p. 27.

28. John Fobes, Interview December 9, 1971.

29. H. M. Phillips, op. cit., p. 48.

30. Henri Dieuzeide, Interview December 9, 1971.

31. The assistance of Claire List in the preparation of this section is gratefully acknowledged.

32. "Status of Approved Projects in the Special Fund Component," UNDP, DP/SF Reports, Series A., No. 68, August 31, 1971, p. 4.

33. *Ibid.*, p. 4.

34. Staff paper, Advisory Panel on Programme Policy, UNDP, mimeo, November 24, 1971, p. 1.

35. *Ibid.*, p. 3.

36. *Ibid.*, p. 4.

37. *Ibid.*, p. 5.

38. *Ibid.*, p. 6.

39. "Status of Approved Projects in the Special Fund Component," UNDP, DP/SF Report, Series A., No. 68, August 31, 1971 and Lloyd Mason, UNDP Senior Technical Adviser, Interview March 7, 1972.

40. James Berna, UNDP Senior Technical Adviser, Interview, March 7, 1972.

41. *Education in Developing Countries*, UK Ministry of Overseas Development, A Review of Current Problems and of British Aid, London, Her Majesty's Stationery Office, 1970.

42. *Ibid.*, p. 16.

43. *Ibid.*, p. 16.

44. *Ibid.*, p. 6.

45. *Ibid.*, p. 21.

46. *Ibid.*, p. 34.

47. J. R. Bunting, Interview June 2, 1971.

48. *Ibid.*

49. *Ibid.*

50. There have been numerous articles on the Open University in educational and broadcasting journals. The best source of official information is the 1972 prospectus of the University. Perhaps the best American factual review and commentary is by Neil Eurich and Barry Schwerkmeyer, Great Britain, *Open University: First Chance, Second Chance, or Last Chance?* Academy for Educational Development, August, 1971.

51. *The Open University,* Report of the Planning Committee to the Secretary of State for Education and Science, (London: Her Majesty's Stationery Office, 1969), p. 13.

52. Richmond Postgate, Interview May 25, 1971.

53. Peter Montagnon, Interview, June 4, 1971.

54. Neil Eurich and Barry Schwenkmeyer, op. cit., p. 24.

55. Richard Postgate, Interview May 25, 1971.

56. This section is based on interviews with P. Satukov, Chief, Department of USSR-TV and four associates, October 14, 1971.

57. There are said to be 2.5 million extension students in the USSR.

58. This section is based on interviews with Rector Fedotov and four associates, October 16, 1971.

59. This section is based on interviews with Deputy (and Acting) Rector Semenov and two associates, October 18, 1971.

60. This section is based on a visit to Israel in mid-December, 1971, and interviews with educators, ETV personnel, and the Minister of Education and Culture.

61. Two key documents contain the basic information on ITC: (a) the Hanadiv Committee report on "The Future of Instructional Television and Related Media in Israel," London, October, 1967, and an ITC Fact Sheet, Tel Aviv, December, 1971.

CHAPTER FIVE

The Conditions of Success

The conditions of success in the use of the things of learning are many, varied, imprecise, changeable, and changing. Within this uncertainty, projects that incorporate certain considerations enhance substantially their likelihood of achieving successs.

A recognized and generally agreed-upon need must exist. Or, as Schramm and his colleagues say, the probability of success is greater if a project "grows out of a critical appraisal of needs and alternative solutions."[1] Although this may appear to be obvious, on several occasions a retrospective examination has evoked the question whether the project warranted the use of instructional technology.

A desire to meet the need and to do it through the use of instructional technology must pervade. The people who must use instructional technology should want to use it and believe in its efficacy. As Keppel and Cornog note, ". . . machine and software combined cannot succeed unless those that use them are convinced they work and should be used."[2] It must be both appropriate and acceptable.[3] Apathy and indifference and damaging, but overt, opposition by those who must use, or be used by, the technology will almost certainly guarantee failure. If the resistance of the teacher is the greatest deterrent to the use of instructional technology, especially and primarily television, then the desire to use technology must either exist or be developed in the teachers; otherwise, instructional technology will fail.

A purpose must guide and must be articulated. If there is no purpose, there should be no project. Both the initiators and the executors must know and comprehend the purpose of the project.

As Morgan puts it: "The cornerstone of instructional technology is the proposition that the goals of education and training can be operationally defined in terms of learner performance."[4] Instructional technology is for the *learner*. Measurable success is more likely to result if the purpose is single rather than multiple; specific rather than general; limited rather than diffuse; unambiguous rather than vague; and agreed upon rather than imposed.

A structure should exist which makes success possible, or at least does not in advance assure failure. A system which is hospitable to instructional technology can enhance its adoption, use, and success; a hostile one can retard or even prevent it. Dietrich and Johnson pinpoint the problem. "Prior to any administrative reorganization to bring about change involving educational technology, certain steps need to be taken. First, change procedures need to be defined; second, a commitment to change must be negotiated and stated; and finally, a climate of change must be developed."[5] Unity of purpose among the authorities responsible for an instructional technology project and broad involvement in the educational system in which the project takes place are two factors, identified by Schramm and his colleagues, that increase the probability of success.[6] The structure alone does not automatically provide either unity of purpose or involvement, but unless the structure is changed positively on both fronts, unity of purpose will be temporary, and involvement minimal.

Leadership must be exerted at the right level of authority, responsibility and control. Strong backing by top authorities is the basic requirement for effecting swift innovation in a school system.[7] Hagerstown had strong leadership from the superintendent of schools and support from the Board of Education.[8] Chicago's Television College had support from the top. Television teaching in American Samoa got under way because the governor sponsored it. El Salvador's television project was supported unreservedly by the Minister of Education. In Israel, the Minister of Education supplied the political support, backed the director general, lobbied for the money, and made the project work.

Teachers must participate and support the project (unless they are to be displaced altogether, a prospect thus far unlikely in any country in which they have a stronghold).[9] Lyle Nelson of Stanford, who has observed and evaluated the American Samoan effort from its beginning, discussed the tendency not to involve the teacher in instructional technology:

. . . the operation essentially began with the decision to use television following which came questions about the role it should play. Obviously this is going about things backward. The much more sensible approach—which everyone endorses but no one seems to follow—would be to define educational objectives and specific classroom objectives *with the classroom teachers involved,* and then to ask what part in meeting these television might play. . . .

Instead of starting with educational needs and objectives and then asking what part instructional television might play in meeting them, what was done in Samoa was essentially to design a new curriculum *for television.* As a result, the role of the classroom teacher was downgraded, very much so, with predictable results. The classroom teacher—by far the most important factor in *any* learning process—became at best an ancillary element and at worst an unwilling and negative participant. It is significant, I think, that in the early stages the project was in the hands of broadcasters and not curriculum specialists.[10]

Some substance must require the use of the things of learning. The medium may affect the message, sometimes drastically, as applications have illustrated. It may even *be* the message, although that is not at issue here. If the technology is as powerful and as essential as its proponents claim, then its content should not be left to chance.

A mechanism for measurement, for evaluation of the experience, must be included. While there have been several reports of research many are old, and most are general and inconclusive. If the focus were sharper, the evaluation would be more precise.

Finally, adequate resources must be provided at the beginning and for the duration of the project. Instructional technology is expensive. Adequate financial resources are critical. Chicago's Television College continues because the Chicago School Board supplies the money. Hagerstown had substantial financial support from the Board of Education. One of the major ingredients in the success of "Sesame Street" and "The Electric Company" has been the ability of the Children's Television Workshop to obtain the level of resources needed for the kind of research and production efforts required to do the job. The Samoan project flourished when funds were forthcoming, and it began to languish when funds were not so plentiful. "Experiments" and "demonstrations" launched by "outside" money usually wither and die when "inside" money must assume the responsibility. The financial resource picture is further complicated by the nature of the use of instructional technology. The things of learning have always been viewed as additional expenses rather than as means to cut costs and/or increase educational effectiveness.[11]

The inclusion of these nine conditions in the planning, execution and evaluation stages of a project will increase its likelihood of success. The prospective user of the things of learning should also be cognizant of four other issues which will bear on the shape and ultimate form of the project.

The first is the appropriate use and amount of technology, the place of the multi-media approach to teaching and learning. Although no one would gainsay that the things of learning can make a definite contribution to the learning experience, the extent and manner of the contribution are concerns yet to be resolved by further experience.

The size of a project is also a consideration. Schramm and his colleagues select as one criterion of success a project of "feasible size."[12] They continue, "There may well be a 'critical mass' beyond which it becomes much easier to introduce instructional television."[13] El Salvador is countrywide; its instructional television project is said to be effective, but it is small. Niger's instructional television project is thought by some to be inherently good, but less effective because it is not countrywide. The question of effective size will remain unanswered until the results of more projects are evaluated.

Local initiative in dealings between aid giving and aid receiving countries or agencies is another consideration. Feldman, in a report on cable television, states the problem:

Ghetto programs often fail for much the same reasons that foreign aid programs fail; to the extent that they appear imposed from the outside, they stifle local initiative, responsibility, and dedication.[14]

While in theory this is obvious, it is often ignored in practice. Frequently the donor has either ideas or money, or both, to peddle; and the donee, loath to appear unresponsive or unappreciative, feigns interest in the concepts to get the funds.

Finally, the prospective user should consider the cost and effort required to utilize the different things of learning in relation to the purpose of the project. While, for many, "instructional technology" means "instructional television," the evidence is not conclusive as to the ways in which instructional television offers greater advantages as an aid to learning. Because the production cost and effort requirements are greater in television, both developed and developing countries should explore some of the other "things of learning."

Notes

1. Wilbur Schramm, Philip H. Coombs, Friedrich Kahnert, Jack Lyle, *The New Media: Memo to Educational Planners*, UNESCO, International Institute for Educational Planning, Paris, 1967, p. 99.

2. Francis Keppel and Michael L. Cornog, "Evaluation and Measurement of Instructional Technology," in Sidney G. Tickton, (ed.) *To Improve Learning Vol II*, (New York and London: R. R. Bowker Company, 1971), p. 825.

3. John E. Dietrich and F. Craig Johnson, "Changes in Administrative Organization Aimed to Effect the Introduction of Appropriate Educational Technology," in Sidney G. Tickton (ed.) *To Improve Learning Vol. II.* (New York and London: R. R. Bowker Company, 1971), p. 476.

4. Robert M. Morgan, "Instructional Technology in Vocational Training," in Sidney G. Tickton (ed.) *To Improve Learning, Vol. II*, (New York and London: R. R. Bowker Company, 1971), p. 781.

5. John E. Dietrich and F. Craig Johnson, *op. cit.*, p. 469.

6. Wilbur Schramm, et al. *op. cit.*, p. 102.

7. *New Educational Media in Action: Case Studies for Planners—I*, (Paris: UNESCO, Institute for Educational Planning, 1967), p. 49.

8. *Ibid.*, p. 82.

9. This of course does not apply if the nature of the instructional technology effort is such that it bypasses the teachers altogether. But even then, they can muster formidable opposition to what is attempted, even when it is wholly outside the system of which they are a part.

10. Private communication.

11. James R. DuMolin and Robert P. Morgan, "An Instructional Satellite System for the United States: Preliminary Considerations," Internal Memorandum No. 71-2, Program on Application of Communications Satellites to Educational Development, (Washington University, July 16, 1971), p. 33.

12. Wilbur Schramm, et al, *op. cit.*, p. 99.

13. New Educational Media in Action, *op. cit.*, p. 81.

14. N. E. Feldman, Cable TV Report, Rand Corporation, "Local Program Origination," R-570-ff-September 1970.

Index